STAR MAPS

Map 1 North Circumpolar Stars
Map 2 Fall and Winter Stars
Map 3 Winter and Spring Stars
Map 4 Spring and Summer Stars

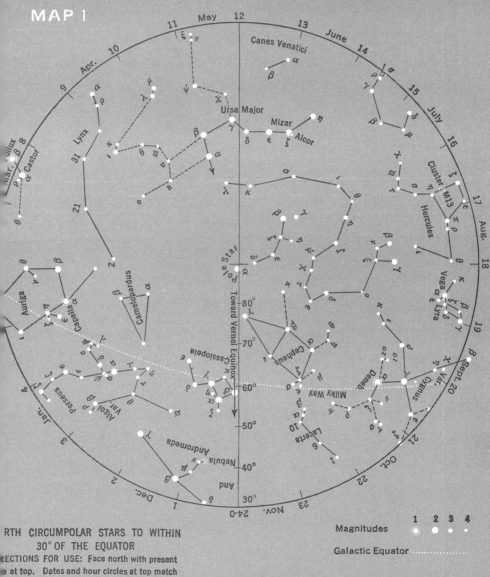

MAP 1

NORTH CIRCUMPOLAR STARS TO WITHIN
30° OF THE EQUATOR

DIRECTIONS FOR USE: Face north with present
date at top. Dates and hour circles at top match
those on north side of the mercator maps.

Magnitudes   1 2 3 4

Galactic Equator ....

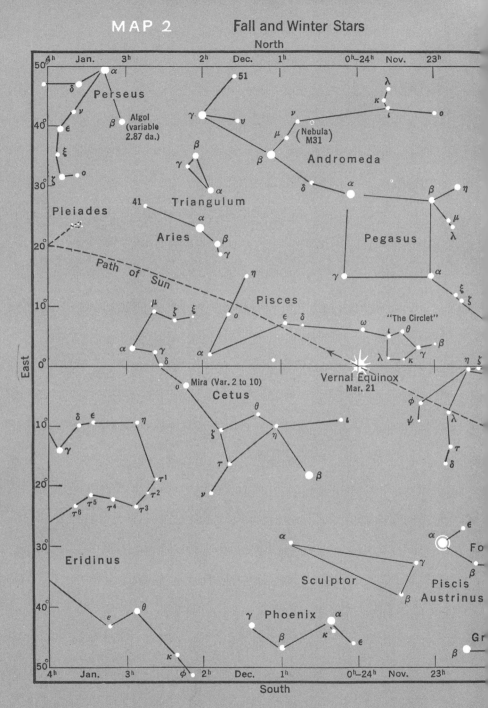

MAP 2   Fall and Winter Stars

North

Perseus

Algol (variable 2.87 da.)

51

Andromeda

(Nebula M31)

Triangulum

Pleiades

41

Aries

Pegasus

Path of Sun

Pisces

"The Circlet"

Mira (Var. 2 to 10)

Cetus

Vernal Equinox
Mar. 21

East

Eridinus

Sculptor

Piscis Austrinus

Fo

Phoenix

Gr

South

DIRECTIONS:
In whichever direction you are looking, hold that edge of the map down. Then raise it above the head if you wish.
The months given at top and bottom of map indicate approximately when these stars are near the meridian at about 8
To extend view northward match hour circles (or months) given at edge of these maps with the upper ones of the polar

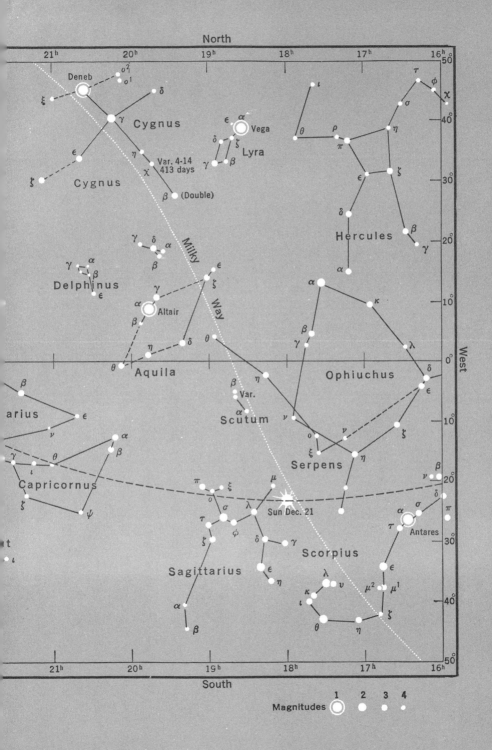

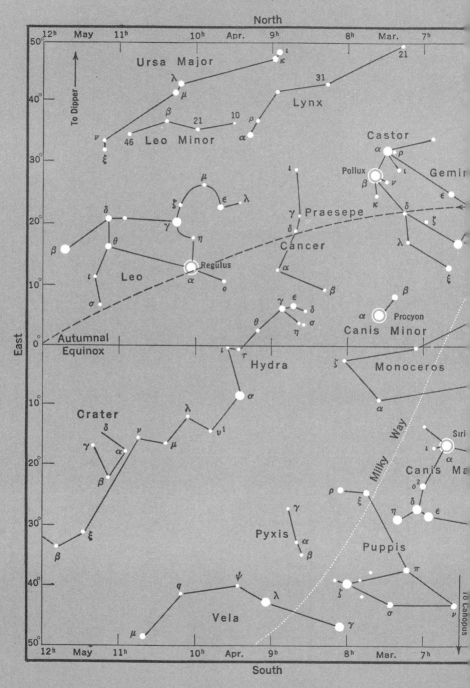

MAP 3   Winter and Spring Stars

(SEE MAP 2 FOR DIRECTIONS)

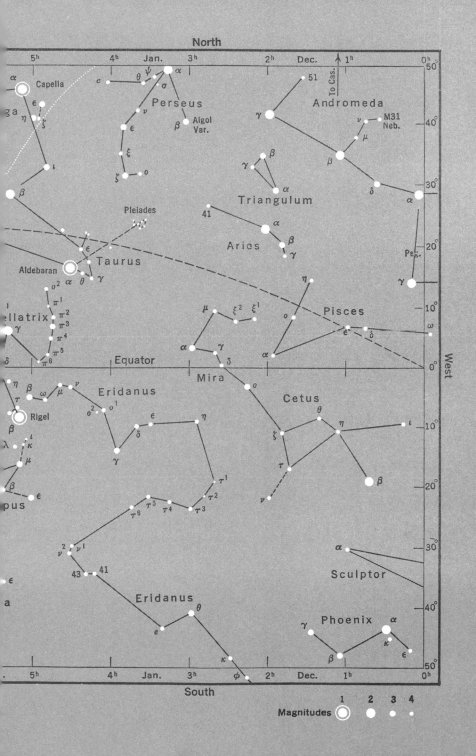

MAP 4   Spring and Summer Stars

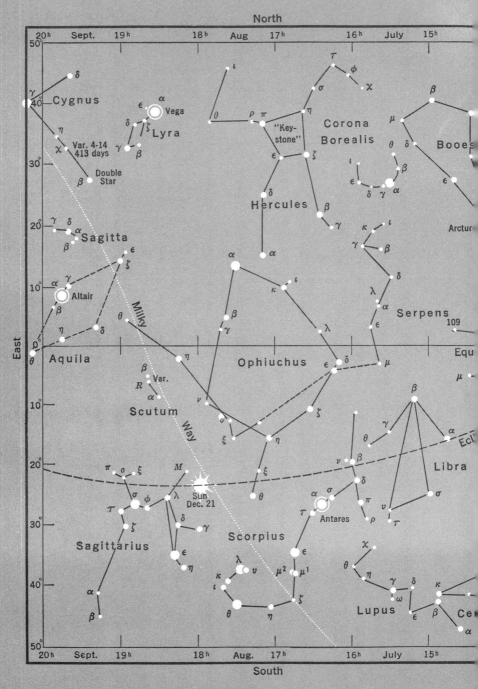

(SEE MAP 2 FOR DIRECTIONS)

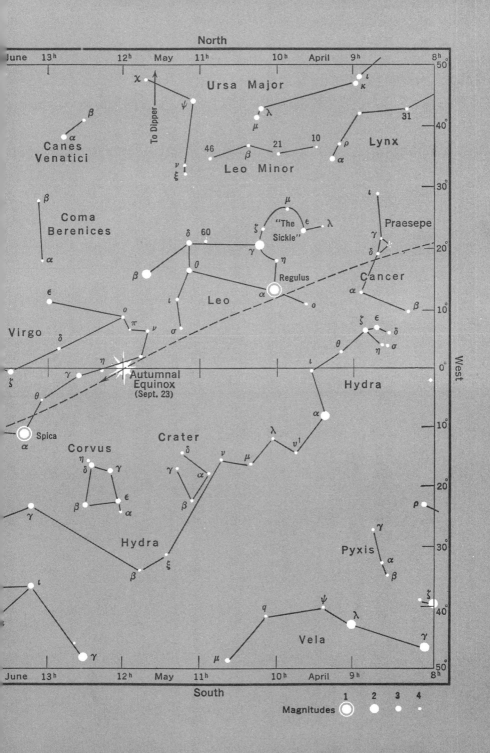

THE FASCINATING WORLD OF ASTRONOMY

1.

2.

5.

6.

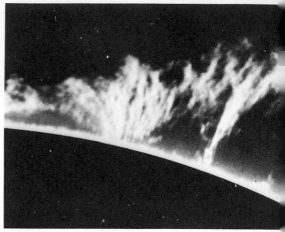

Books by
Robert S. Richardson

*The Fascinating World
of Astronomy*

Exploring Mars

Second Satellite

Sun, Moon, and Stars
(with William T. Sk

7.

3.

4.

THE FASCINATING WORLD
OF ASTRONOMY

Robert S. Richardson, *Associate Director,*
Griffith Observatory and Planetarium, Los Angeles

McGraw-Hill Book Company, Inc.
NEW YORK   TORONTO   LONDON

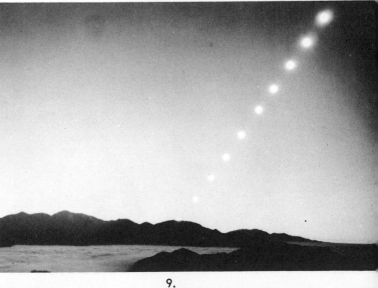

9.

Key to illustrations on title page
1. The Schmidt telescope, Figure 4, page 8
2. The edge of the sun, Figure 39, page 85
3. Irregular nebula in Cygnus, Figure 103, page 256
4. Crescent moon and Saturn, Figure 23, page 50
5. Finsler's comet, Figure 71, page 167
6. Dome of the telescope on Palomar, Figure 2, page 5
7. The great galaxy in Andromeda, Figure 98, page 246
8. Jupiter, Figure 62, page 140
9. Successive images of the sun, Figure 14, page 33

THE FASCINATING WORLD OF ASTRONOMY

Printed in the United States of America.
Copyright © 1960 by Robert S. Richardson.
All rights reserved. This book or parts
thereof may not be reproduced in any form
without written permission of the publishers.

Library of Congress Catalog Card Number: 60-6981

Litho in U.S.A. by Mahony & Roese Inc.

This book is for Marjorie and Rae

▶ PREFACE

It used to be that when an astronomer went to a party there was one question he was almost sure to be asked: "Why did you ever become an astronomer, anyhow?"

For a long time the work of an astronomer was regarded as so far removed from everyday life that people were puzzled that anyone should voluntarily adopt such an out-of-the-way profession. The astronomer himself was looked upon as something of a curiosity, a being who rarely descended from his elevated heights to converse with ordinary mortals. Most astronomers, of course, have no desire to appear unusual. They are for the most part rather retiring people whose chief desire is to be left alone so they can work in peace.

True, in the past this work seemed to have scant connection with daily events, so the question often proved embarrassing. It was hard to explain to people that while your work might not be of any immediate practical value it nonetheless thoroughly fascinated *you*—that you looked upon your job not so much as work as a hobby, something that interested you so much it was hard to leave it alone even on your vacation. Unfortunately, this sort of enthusiasm is hard to impart to other people. Therefore the astronomer often preferred not to mention it at all, and most of what was written about astronomy came from people who were not themselves astronomers and therefore had only secondhand knowledge of the subject matter.

Within recent years, however, a most amazing transformation has taken place. Instead of being considered far removed from ordinary life, astronomy is now the subject of almost daily articles in the newspapers. In advertisements both men and machines are depicted working against a background of stars, which is supposed to show the forward-looking attitude of the employer or manufacturer. Such words as *satellite* and *orbit* have become commonplaces in newspaper headlines. People no longer think of the moon,

Mars, or Venus as bodies forever separated from the earth by a void, but look upon them with much the same sort of personal interest they might take in a new real-estate development they are considering for a homesite. Artificial satellites have opened new regions for exploration in the outer fringes of the atmosphere and beyond. Atomic physicists now find some of their most interesting problems occurring in the stars and nebulae. Powerful radio receivers have made us conscious of a flood of radiation reaching us from outer space that, a few short years back, we never even dreamed existed.

As a result, whether he likes it or not, today the astronomer finds himself engaged frequently and publicly in answering questions about his science. No longer is he a remote, isolated figure. In fact, through lectures and other public appearances the astronomer has become rather glamorous, much better known than scientists in many other research fields.

The sudden advent of the space age has imbued a large number of people with the desire to learn something about the wonders of the universe, so rapidly unfolding around them. Many of these newly interested people desire information but do not know exactly how to obtain it. They usually do not have time or inclination to read the fairly formidable textbooks that cover the whole subject of astronomy in a formal, comprehensive manner. As adults they dislike reading the "star books" written for children. What they wish most of all is simply to have an astronomer tell them about some of the fascinating things in the sky.

We have tried to do just this, by writing a book in the form of questions and answers. As such, it does not attempt to cover all the subject matter of astronomy or to serve as a complete reference work. A comparatively few subjects have been selected and treated at some length, with the discussion on an informal basis. So far as possible, each question is complete in itself. You should be able to dip into *The Fascinating World of Astronomy* almost anywhere and find something of interest.

Robert S. Richardson

▶ CONTENTS

1 ▶ ASTRONOMERS
AND THEIR WORK

▶ *How do you become an astronomer?*

The work of an astronomer is so far removed from that of most other occupations that most people have only the vaguest idea of what it really consists of, much less how one proceeds to enter the profession. From personal acquaintance, most people know how one becomes a doctor or dentist, a salesman or engineer. But they have probably never met an astronomer—and would not know where to find one. This is not too surprising; it is doubtful that there are more than a thousand professional astronomers in the world, and only a few hundred of these are actively engaged in research work. Our new knowledge of the heavenly bodies is gained through the efforts of only a few individuals. People who have visited large observatories know that astronomers work inside curious dome-shaped buildings where telescopes are housed, but you would hardly walk into one off the street and ask for a job, as you might to apply for work in a store or factory.

Actually, there is no more mystery about becoming an astronomer than there is about becoming a chemist or a geologist. You would study at some college or university that has a strong department of astronomy—the University of California, for example, or Harvard, or the California Institute of Technology. You could even become an astronomer without having taken much astronomy as an undergraduate: a good background in physics and mathematics is much more essential; the astronomy can be picked up later. In fact, some astronomers have started out as physicists and later found problems in the stars that interested them so much they moved over into astronomy. Actually, at present there is no essential difference between the work of the physicist and that of the

1

astronomer. Both are engaged in the study of atoms, molecules, and nuclear reactions—the physicist in his laboratory, the astronomer in his observatory with his telescope. The new field of radio astronomy in particular is one that would seem to belong more to the physicist than the astronomer.

Today it is absolutely necessary for anyone who aspires to become a professional astronomer to earn the degree of Doctor of Philosophy. This means that he will have to go to college for about four years as an undergraduate, and at least three more as a graduate student to obtain his Ph.D. Besides astronomy, during these seven years he will be taking courses in mathematics, optics, spectroscopy, electronics, nuclear physics, and related subjects. He will probably also at some time take courses in machine shop and mechanical drawing, since an astronomer often needs to design instruments, or at least be able to tell others the type of instruments he wants. Many people assume that an astronomer spends all his time with his head pointed toward the stars and has little contact with hard reality. Most astronomers actually do a good deal of work with their hands—adjusting instruments at the telescope or trying to find the source of difficulty when a piece of equipment refuses to work. An astronomer should therefore include among his college courses some that will enable him to work with his hands as well as his head.

During his last year a graduate student must do original research in some subject that particularly interests him, usually one in the field in which he intends eventually to specialize. This research work constitutes his thesis, and selecting a suitable subject often poses quite a problem. It will preferably be one that can be completed in a year, so that he can get his degree after the usual three years of study, but sometimes a student has to devote two or more years to it. It will be a definite advantage if the university he attends has good telescopic and other equipment, so that he can get firsthand experience in working with astronomical instruments. If the thesis work results in something of genuine value, and especially if it is published in one of the astronomical journals, it may attract attention and be of considerable practical help in obtaining the budding astronomer a position.

After he receives his doctorate there still remains for the graduate the problem of finding a job. This is not nearly as difficult as it

2

used to be; there are now openings for astronomers in many military projects as well as with firms engaged in space research. As before, however, most openings are still in the astronomy departments of universities, so that—whether he likes it or not—a considerable part of the young astronomer's time will have to be devoted to teaching. For advancement in most universities a professor must continue original research in addition to his teaching duties. This research will frequently have to be done in his spare time or during summer vacations. An astronomy professor can sometimes obtain leave of absence after he has become established to work at an observatory where a powerful telescope is available.

This has begun to sound as if becoming an astronomer is a rather formidable business after all, and there is no denying that it is not altogether easy. Most new Ph.D.s, however, will admit that on the whole they had a pretty stimulating time during their graduate work, especially if some of it was done with a large telescope and modern equipment. Learning can be a more fascinating process than loafing. There is a great deal of satisfaction in feeling that you are gaining ground and acquiring new knowledge as you go along. Often, too, there are scholarships available that help pay living expenses. If the young astronomer today is expected to know more than his predecessors did, there are also more favorable opportunities in exciting fields of research waiting for him when he graduates than were dreamed of in the past.

▶ How does a large observatory operate?

Anyone who strolls about the grounds of a large observatory is struck by the fact that it is one of the most deserted places he has ever visited. The dome-shaped buildings are impressive, but nobody appears to be bustling about doing anything in them. A few people who look like workmen enter or leave the domes, but there is nobody in sight who has the appearance of an astronomer. Not being sure just how an astronomer should look, the visitor has the feeling that one would at least look important. It seems incredible that such a large place should be so devoid of life.

If you visit an observatory in the morning, the place is deserted because the astronomers are all asleep. The only people stirring will be a maintenance man and a janitor because only a few people

are required to keep an observatory running. The astronomer and his assistant close the dome and go to bed at dawn, about the time other people are thinking of getting up. They sleep till noon—or try to sleep, since it is not always possible to change your sleeping habits abruptly. They get up about noon and have breakfast when most other people are eating lunch.

At some observatories—such as Lick near San Jose, California —the astronomers and their families have homes on the mountain-top from which they observe. At others—such as Mount Wilson and Palomar Mountain—the astronomers live in nearby Pasadena, and travel to the mountain only when they wish to observe. At Mount Wilson and Palomar Mountain the astronomers and other people connected with the observatory eat and sleep while they are "on duty" in quarters specially provided for them and called "the Monastery." This name was first applied to the Mount Wilson living quarters; later, when the 200-inch telescope was erected on Palomar, the term was borrowed for staff quarters there. According to one story, the name originated in the fact that three of the

4

men who worked on Mount Wilson in the early days were called Abbot, Monk, and St. John.

A schedule, made out about three weeks in advance, assigns astronomers to the telescope according to their particular observing programs. For example, at Mount Wilson a man may have five nights at the 60-inch telescope, after which he transfers to the 100-inch telescope for another five nights. Then he goes down the mountain as someone else comes up from town to take his place.

After lunch the astronomer will probably return to the dome to look over the results of the previous night's observation. Perhaps he still has some photographic plates to develop. Or maybe something had gone wrong with his apparatus so that practically the whole night was wasted; if so, he will be busy inside the dome

1. *Left:* The dome of the 100-inch telescope of the Mount Wilson Observatory.

2. *Below:* The dome of the 200-inch telescope on Palomar Mountain seen by moonlight.

during the afternoon tracing the trouble in order to be ready to start his observations that night. There is always something to do: an instrument to be adjusted, film plates to be cut, a lost filter to be located. This is likely to keep him busy till dinner time, so that he has to rush down to the Monastery and wash up in a hurry.

At the dinner table he joins people who have come up the mountain for various purposes. There will be another astronomer or two (working at the other telescope), the engineer who keeps the equipment running, and the astronomers who work during the day observing the sun. Since the tasks are so diverse, they seldom see each other except at mealtime. Dinner-table conversation may cover any topic; sometimes it is a lively discussion of a scientific problem, but more often the talk is light and deals with an incident that happened during the day or an item in the news.

Since the astronomers come and go during the week as they take turns at the telescope, the faces around the dinner table are never all the same. This is one of the best features about living in town

3. Astronomer putting photographic plates in oven for baking. Heating the plates for several days considerably increases their sensitivity to light.

and going on the mountain only when you have to observe—you don't see enough of any individual for minor personal differences to arise. It is difficult to live in semi-isolation as members of a small group for a long time without friction of some kind developing. But when people are always coming and going this is largely avoided. (Incidentally, this difficulty of living in isolation with the same few people may well be one of the grave problems we will have to solve if we ever succeed in establishing stations on the moon or Mars. We *could* conquer space and then be unable to make the most of our conquest because we could not get along with one another.)

If it is summer, the astronomer will have a couple of hours of leisure before it grows dark enough to go to work. But in the late fall and winter it is dark enough to go to work immediately. So in winter he changes into warmer clothes immediately after dinner and heads for the unheated dome. Here he will probably find the night assistant waiting for him; in fact, the assistant may already have the telescope set on the first object for the night's observation.

The astronomer's first concern will be with the "seeing." This refers to the steadiness of the atmosphere. If the air is calm, so that the star images appear as sharp points of light, the seeing is said to be good. But if the star images are blurred and dancing about due to air currents—as is too often the case—seeing is pronounced bad. If it is too bad, the astronomer may not be able to work at all, even if the atmosphere is perfectly clear, in which case he has no choice but to close up the dome and go to bed.

We will suppose that the seeing is pretty good tonight and the astronomer has high hopes of getting in a good night's work. So let us say he loads a plateholder and focuses the telescope on a star near the object on which he intends to work. After focusing the telescope, he switches to the object in which he is interested, attaches the plateholder to the telescope, and when all is in readiness pulls the slide, thus starting the photographic exposure. The exposure may last for a few minutes or several hours, depending upon the brightness of the object and the type of photography he is using. Or the astronomer may not be photographing at all; he may be working with a photoelectric device, registering the light from a star by means of the photocell on a recording instrument. If all goes well, by dawn he may have obtained a fine set of

4. The 48-inch Schmidt telescope on Palomar Mountain.

observations and can go to bed feeling very much pleased with himself. On the other hand, instrumental difficulties may develop to upset the whole night's program. Or perhaps clouds came over in the middle of an exposure, forcing him to suspend operations. If this happens on his last scheduled night at the telescope, it may be a month before he will have another chance to observe the objects he missed tonight. If he has bad luck on several occasions, the sun may begin to come so near his special stars that he has to wait a whole year before he has a chance to observe it again.

8

As he drives down the mountain after lunch, the clouds that may have prevented observations during the night are clearing away and the sun is shining brightly. It looks as if the astronomer who just came up will have a fine run.

▶ *What does an astronomer do when he is not observing at the telescope?*

In a few nights, with good luck, an astronomer may be able to get enough observations to keep him busy working in his office for weeks or even months. Let us take a rather simple example and suppose he has obtained some photographs of an asteroid, or little planet. It might be an interesting little asteroid like Icarus, which at its closest approach to the sun comes within the orbit of Mercury and at its greatest distance goes out beyond the orbit of Mars. Now he wants to determine where Icarus is located in relation to fixed stars on the photographic plate, whose positions are accurately known. (The stars may be considered as fixed in positions in the sky, except for *very* slow motions which need

5. An astronomer examining the plates he has taken at the telescope the night before.

not concern us here.) First he has to identify the stars in his photographs from their numbers recorded in a catalogue. Next he puts the plate on a measuring machine and measures the relative position of the asteroid to these stars. Then from the known positions of the stars the position of the asteroid at the time the plate was exposed can be found.

All this may require considerable time. Simply identifying the catalogued stars may be the work of several days. Measuring the plates may also take several days. Finally, calculating the position of the asteroid in a form that can be transmitted to other astronomers will take a day or two. In all, a week may easily be spent in "reducing" some plates that were taken at the telescope in a few hours' time. It is, of course, impossible to say how much office work may go into reducing plates taken at the telescope, since the time varies with the nature of the work. In any case, the astronomer almost always spends more time at his desk than he does at the telescope.

▶ *Do all astronomers work at the telescope?*

Some astronomers seldom, if ever, work at a telescope. They are "desk astronomers" whose work is largely theoretical and requires a great deal of mathematics. They take the

10

6. Astronomer at measuring machine, examining a photograph he has taken at the telescope.

results of the work of observational astronomers and try to interpret them or fit them into an existing theory. Since this work requires exceptional ability in both mathematics and physics, few astronomers engage in it alone. The work of the theoretical astronomer serves as a guide to the men who make observations. It often indicates what sort of observations are the most likely to yield significant results.

For example, about 1944 a young Dutch astrophysicist named Henrik C. van de Hulst predicted from theory that hydrogen atoms in interstellar space would radiate waves 21 centimeters (about 8 inches) in length and that these waves might be detected by highly sensitive radio receivers. In 1951 a receiver was finally built with which the 21-centimeter line of hydrogen was actually detected according to prediction. Observations with the 21-centimeter line of hydrogen have made it possible to probe distances in the galaxy still far beyond our reach with ordinary optical methods. Thus the desk work of a theoretical astronomer indicated the direction observational astronomers should take to open new pathways for exploration in the sky.

▶ *Is there a place for women in astronomy?*

Often the work of an astronomer consists of making measurements of the same general type on a series of photographs of certain stars on his observing program. The measurement and reduction of these plates is not difficult but is time-consuming and tedious. The routine measuring is often turned over to assistants and clerks who work at the observatory; many of these are women. But this detailed and monotonous work, which consists of doing the same thing over and over, can hardly be called astronomy, except for the subject. Actually there are few women today who study the stars as real astronomers.

It is rather surprising how few women take up astronomical work, considering the number who study it as students. College professors of astronomy are accustomed to classes in which nearly half the students are women. They learn about the stars and planets, compare time sets, and check each other's comet orbits. At least there is no prejudice against women in astronomy, unless it is on the part of the public. I still recall with amusement the be-

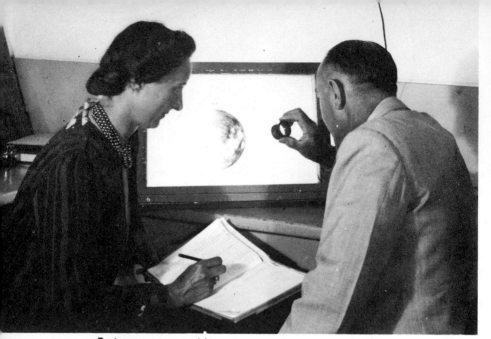

7. An astronomer and his assistant examining image of moon. It is generally as assistants that women work in professional astronomy today.

wildered expression on the faces of visitors to the Lick Observatory when, instead of being greeted by a bewhiskered old professor, as they had expected, they were given a lecture on the heavenly bodies by a girl scarcely old enough to vote.

A few women have achieved prominence in astronomy. For example, Madame Jean André Lepaute, wife of a famous French clockmaker, with the astronomers Alexis Claude Clairaut and Joseph Jérôme Lalande engaged in a race against time with Halley's comet, in an effort to fix the date the comet would pass nearest the sun in 1758. They computed morning and night, sometimes even at meals; the assistance of Madame Lepaute was invaluable.

Another woman who has become famous in astronomy is the sister of the great Sir William Herschel, Caroline Herschel, who "minded the heavens" for her brother. In 1828 she was elected an honorary member and awarded the gold medal of the British Royal Astronomical Society. Considering how reluctant scientific societies have been to accord recognition to women, this must be considered a signal honor.

Among the classics of science are the papers on the spectra of the stars, nebulae, and comets by Sir William Huggins and Margaret Lindsay Murray, Lady Huggins. Lady Huggins became so interested in astronomy at an early age that she built a spectroscope from a description in a magazine article. Upon her marriage in 1875 she devoted herself entirely to aiding her husband, so that eventually they published their papers together. In 1903 Lady Margaret was elected an honorary member of the Royal Astronomical Society, the fourth woman at that time to have been given such recognition.

The first notable woman astronomer in the United States was Maria Mitchell, born in Nantucket in 1818, at a time when few men in her neighborhood had much learning. At the age of twelve she helped her father take astronomical observations and was studying conic sections at seventeen. Her unusual training in this era was largely a result of the fact that for generations her family had been Quakers, a people who from the beginning have believed in the then-extraordinary doctrine of equal education for men and women.

Until she was forty-seven, Miss Mitchell's chief astronomical work was helping her father with his government surveys for latitude and longitude, but she also helped with systematic observations of the planets, sunspots, meteors, and auroral clouds. In 1847 she discovered a comet for which the King of Denmark presented her with a medal "to the value of twenty ducats." A year later she became the first woman elected to the American Academy of Arts and Sciences. It is said that a serious discussion arose over the propriety of referring to Miss Mitchell as a "Fellow" of the Society, a question finally settled by erasing the word on her diploma and inserting "Honorary Member" in its place.

Among more recent women astronomers are Miss Annie J. Cannon, Miss Antonia C. Maury, and Miss Henrietta S. Leavitt, who did remarkable work on the Harvard Observatory staff during the last half century. The present chairman of the Department of Astronomy at Harvard University is a woman, Mrs. Cecilia Payne-Gaposchkin.

We noted that nearly as many women as men do postgraduate work in astronomy. Yet the total number of women actively engaged in astronomical research today is small. The reason for this mysterious discrepancy is not too hard to find. Most of them become astronomers' wives instead of astronomers!

▶ Do astronomers specialize
in their study of the heavens?

Yes, indeed! Astronomers have minutely divided up the different objects in the heavens among themselves. They study intensively the particular type of object that interests them the most and may have only a casual knowledge of what is going on in other fields.

During the last century astronomy was concerned chiefly with the accurate determination of the positions of the heavenly bodies in space and paid little attention to the nature of these bodies. For example, a century ago the little planetary bodies called asteroids that revolve mostly between the orbits of Mars and Jupiter were objects of much interest. Their paths among the stars were carefully plotted so that their orbits around the sun could be accurately calculated. The discovery of a new asteroid was a major event; astronomers got busy immediately with their telescopes determining its position so that it would not be lost. Similarly, the discovery of a new comet meant that numerous observations were made of its position in relation to the fixed stars, for the determination of its orbit. Other astronomers were largely engaged in getting better positions of the stars to serve as reference points in the sky for the determination of time, which used to be one of the chief functions of an observatory. Still others tried to improve the tables of the motions of the planets so that there would be a closer agreement between theory and observation.

Thus it can be seen that formerly astronomers were chiefly concerned with the *where* and *when* of the heavenly bodies; that is, where these bodies were at a particular time, so that their positions at a future date could be calculated. The heavenly bodies were regarded as far as possible as points moving upon the surface of the celestial sphere; it was the astronomer's business to keep track of them to the best of his ability. Astronomy was so limited in scope that it was possible for one man to have a pretty good general idea of the whole of it. The instruments and methods of observation were few and simple enough to be easily mastered.

Thus in the last century an astronomer's interests were wide enough to extend over almost the whole range of objects in the sky.

In the latter half of the nineteenth century, however, a few astronomers began experimenting with the *spectroscope,* which breaks up the light of the heavenly bodies into a rainbow beam, from which it is possible to determine the chemical elements that compose them. This work on the spectra of the heavenly bodies, starting slowly, gradually developed until by the early part of the twentieth century it began to supersede the astronomy of position. Different kinds of objects were found to give different types of spectra; blue stars, for example, gave a different spectrum from red stars. Also, the glowing clouds of gas in the Milky Way called the nebulae gave quite a different type of spectrum from the stars. Astronomers found such a wealth of material for study among the spectra of the stars that they began to specialize in certain types to the exclusion of others. The study of the spectra of the nebulae became a special field in itself. The sun is so close to us and so bright that its spectrum can be studied in much more detail than that of the stars and nebulae. Not only has the spectrum of the sun become an object of special study; the sun itself has been divided up into different sections. Some astronomers now specialize in the study of the outer atmosphere of the sun (corona), while others concentrate on such surface details as the spots and the solar granulations. Technical advances today are continually opening up fields for specialized study, as the spectroscope did a century ago. Thus the discovery of radio waves emanating from the Milky Way has given rise to a specialized field of research almost as important as that revealed by the telescope more than three centuries ago.

It is curious today to think that only about a century ago there seemed practically nothing left to do in astronomy but chart positions and measure distances. The outstanding problems of the motions of the heavenly bodies had been solved by application of the law of gravitation. Thus about 1840 when Heinrich Schwabe announced the eleven-year rise and fall in the number of sunspots, it was hailed as something new in the "exhausted" science of astronomy! Today, progress in astronomy is so rapid that it is hard for a man to keep up even in his own specialized field.

Most people consider our moon and the planets the most interesting objects in the sky and are surprised and rather shocked to discover that few astronomers pay any attention to them. Most astronomers are occupied exclusively with the stars and nebulae. Few have been attracted to "fundamental" astronomy, which has to do with the determination of the positions and motions of the stars, planets, and satellites. The problems in this field are either so difficult that they defy solution, or consist of the rather routine investigation of the motions of comets and asteroids. Quite recently, however, there has been a dramatic revival of interest in gravitational astronomy as an aftermath of the launching of artificial satellites and other experiments connected with space travel. This has practically wrought a revolution in this field, with the peculiar result that many people working in it today did not start out as astronomers, but are physicists and mathematicians who got into astronomy more or less by accident. The application of electronic methods of computing the motion of a small body moving near the planets has also marked a big advance in gravitational astronomy.

Shortly after the turn of the twentieth century, interest in the stars as personalities instead of geometrical points of light was awakened—largely by discoveries with the spectroscope. It is enough to say here that the spectroscope is a device, attached to the end of a telescope, which spreads the light of a star out into a rainbow band called a *spectrum.* This band is crossed by dark (and sometimes bright) lines produced by the different chemical elements in the star's atmosphere. There seems to be virtually no limit to the amount of information that can be obtained from a detailed study of these dark spectrum lines. No wonder young astronomers began abandoning position astronomy in favor of the vastly more exciting astronomy of the stars as physical bodies, or *astrophysics.* Every object in the sky whose spectrum could be photographed became a problem of interest.

The first job—as usual in science—was one of classification, in this case trying to classify the stars according to their spectra. Father Angelo Secchi had found as early as about 1860 that stars could be divided roughly into four main spectral types. Early investigators such as Secchi in Italy had to observe the spectrum of a star visually with an instrument called a spectro*scope*. This was so difficult that it is hardly surprising that most astronomers shied away from such observing methods. But after about 1900 advances in photography made it possible to record the spectrum of a star on a photographic plate. This constituted an enormous advance, since it gave a permanent record of the star's spectrum which could be studied at leisure. Also, much fainter stars could be studied in this manner than could be observed by the eye.

In the course of classifying the stars according to their spectra, some were found that did not fit into the general scheme, especially variable stars—those whose light changes. Such exceptional cases are always more interesting than the commonplace, so some astronomers began observing only the variable stars. Soon even this proved too much of a job and astronomers began parceling out the variable stars among themselves. Some became "eclipsing variable" men, specializing in those stars whose light varies because they have a dark companion revolving around them which eclipses them regularly. Others observed stars whose light varies regularly in a period of several days, like the star Delta Cephei. Still others became "long-period" variable men, studying the red stars whose light changes are only roughly regular in periods of several months or even years.

Some astronomers found a rich field for study in the different kinds of gaseous nebulae within our Milky Way, such as the ring nebula in the constellation of Lyra or the Crab nebula in Taurus. Others went much farther out into space, beyond our Milky Way system, to study other galaxies or universes of stars such as the galaxy in Andromeda. This study extends to galaxies so distant that they appear as mere smudges on photographs taken with the largest telescopes, and whose distances are estimated in hundreds of millions of light years.

The sun is the nearest star to the earth, the only one whose surface we can study. It is a common sort of star, only a little above average luminosity, and there is no reason to think it differs essentially from other stars of the same spectral type. It might seem that we would soon run out of things to study about a single star, but there are many more things about the sun that puzzle us today than when Galileo first turned his telescope on it more than three hundred years ago. Astronomers who work with the sun keep different hours from others because they must observe during the day. Otherwise there is little difference in the techniques they employ. Because the sun is such a bright source of light it can be studied with much more powerful instruments than those used for the stars. Thus solar astronomers can photograph the dark lines in the spectrum of the sun on a vastly larger scale than is possible with more distant stars. From such studies they have identified more than sixty chemical elements in the atmosphere of the sun. Others are also believed to be present but in such small quantities that they cannot be detected in the sun's spectrum. Observation of the sun includes study of the different features on its surface, such as the dark spots, the clouds that show on solar photographs taken in the light of hydrogen and calcium only, as well as the granulations that make up the surface of the sun. Finally there is the pearly white envelope, called the corona, that flashes out around the sun at the time of a total solar eclipse. Recently a powerful new tool has become available in the study of the sun—the radio telescope, with which the solar atmosphere can be probed in ways impossible with an ordinary optical telescope.

Only a few astronomers do their work on the moon and planets. The moon is probably the most neglected object in the heavens. In fact, astronomers who take direct photographs of the stars regard the moon as a nuisance because its light fogs their plates and prevents them from working for half the month. Often the only time the telescope at a large observatory is turned on the moon is when an important person turns up who has to be shown a spectacular object. Probably one reason the moon is so badly neglected is because nothing—or practically nothing—ever happens there. The moon is so near that its surface features can be studied in minute detail. The visible surface of the moon has been much more accurately mapped than some parts of our own globe. The moon is so close it hardly seems an astronomical body. The study of its surface features belongs more properly to the geologist or physical chemist than to the astronomer.

Most people suppose that when Mars swings near, astronomers drop their regular work and observe nothing else. As a matter of fact, at most large observatories few astronomers ever bother to look at Mars unless they have some spare time between stars in their own program and there is nothing else to do. There are very few "planetary" men. Again, as in the case of the moon, the lack of interest probably stems from the fact that, while there is such a diversity of interesting objects to investigate among the stars and nebulae, the planets remain essentially the same year after year. A student who wishes to select a subject for his doctor's thesis can always find a good one among the stars and nebulae, but good research problems among the planets are extremely scarce.

2 ▶ TELESCOPES
AND MEASUREMENTS

▶ *What does a telescope do?*

The primary purpose of a telescope is to gather light from a distant object and bring this light to a focus so as to form an image of the object. It may also be used to magnify distant objects, and it should be made so that it can be pointed at them with great accuracy, in the case of an astronomical telescope. But the main purpose of a telescope is to gather light. There are two ways to do this. One is to use a glass lens that is thicker at the center than at the edges. The glass bends or refracts the rays of light passing through it so that they come to a common point or focus where the image is formed. This type of telescope has a lens in the end and is called a refractor. (Fig. 8.) We may put a sensitive plate at the position of the image and make a photograph of it, in which case the lens is used essentially as a camera. Or we may put an eyepiece at the position of the image and see a magnified image of it. A telescope may be used either for viewing an object or as a camera simply by interchanging the eyepiece and the photographic plate. Astronomical telescopes are used principally as large cameras for photographing objects in the sky, and only incidentally for looking at magnified images of them with an eyepiece. A photograph gives a permanent record which can be examined and measured years later, reproduced, and studied by other people. A look at an object merely tells how it appeared to one person at a particular time. For this reason astronomers today seldom take more than a casual glance into the eyepiece to make sure the telescope is pointed at the right object.

In gathering light the second way, instead of a lens we may use a mirror to bring rays from a distant object to a focus to form

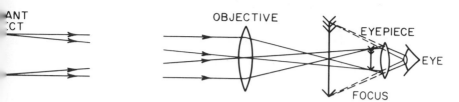

ANT
CT

OBJECTIVE

EYEPIECE

EYE

FOCUS

8. In a lens or refracting telescope the image is formed by bending the rays to a focus. An enlarged view of the image may through the lens be obtained through a magnifier.

an image. The mirror is shaped somewhat like a saucer. The telescope that uses this principle is called a reflector. Until recently the reflector was not so well known as the refractor, but it is becoming more popular in the small-telescope field; it is easier and less expensive to grind a mirror to the proper shape than to grind the lenses for a refracting telescope. Also, mirror telescopes can be made much larger than refractors. It is hard to produce a large piece of glass of good optical quality. The larger the lens the thicker it must be in the center, so that more light is absorbed in passing through it. A lens must be supported around its outside edge, and large heavy lenses bend under their own weight and distort the image. The largest refracting telescope in existence is 40 inches in diameter. The largest reflector is 200 inches in diameter, and there are half a dozen mirrors 60 inches or more in size.

9. The objective or image-forming lens in a 6-inch refracting telescope.

The larger the lens or mirror the more light it will gather. Picture the rays of light from a star as being like raindrops falling from the sky. The telescope might be compared to a funnel spread out over a great area so that it catches many raindrops and brings them together in one stream. Thus the image of a star appears as a bright point of light at the focus of a telescope, because the lens catches many of the rays from a star and concentrates them into points of light which are the images of the stars. The reason these star images look brighter than they do to the eye is that the telescope can catch so many more rays than the human eye can. The amount of light a telescope intercepts from a star will naturally depend upon the size of the object glass or mirror used. (The bigger the funnel the more raindrops are caught.) The eye cannot intercept much light since the opening in the eye is only about one fifth of an inch in diameter.

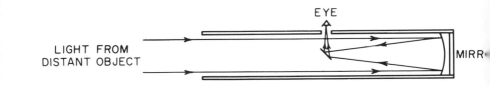

EYE

LIGHT FROM
DISTANT OBJECT

MIRR

10. In a reflecting telescope the rays are bent to a focus by the curved surface of a mirror. Here an auxiliary mirror inside the tube reflects the rays to the eye.

11. An engineer examines a mirror at the top of a 150-foot sun-tower telescope of the Mount Wilson Observatory.

12. An observer works in the prime-focus cage of 200-inch Hale telescope (Palomar Mountain). The surface of the mirror can be seen below.

Let us compare the eye's light-gathering power with that of a telescope having a lens 1 inch in diameter. The relative area of the telescope and eye exposed to starlight is proportional to the square of their diameters or apertures. One fifth of an inch squared is 1/25. One inch squared is still 1 inch. This means that a 1-inch telescope has twenty-five times the light-gathering power of the eye. Similarly, a 10-inch telescope would have 10 squared, or 100 times the light-gathering power of a 1-inch telescope, or 2500 times that of the eye. We see that the light-gathering power of a telescope increases rapidly with its size. Thus the 200-inch mirror should have just about a million times the light-gathering power of the eye. The light-gathering power of a telescope is not strictly proportional to its size, however. Some light is lost by absorption as it passes through a lens and some light is also lost at a mirror surface by reflection. Also, in the case of a reflector, smaller mirrors have to be put within the telescope tube so that the beam can be bent to one side and brought to a focus outside the tube where the astronomer can view it. These mirrors naturally intercept some light and this cuts down the effective aperture of the telescope.

The situation is somewhat different when we attempt to photograph an object with a bright surface, such as the moon, instead of a point of light like a star. In photographing the stars it makes little difference how much magnification is used, since we simply spread the star images farther apart. The points of light are still points of light, no matter where they appear. But magnification makes a great difference when we photograph an object that extends over a surface, like the moon. The greater the surface over which we spread the image the fainter it will be. Thus we can secure more size or magnification only at the expense of getting a fainter image to work with.

▶ *Upon what does the size of the image depend?*

The size of the image depends only upon the focal length of the telescope. The longer the focal length (or the farther the image is formed from the lens or mirror), the larger the image will be. If we have a bright source of light like the sun, we can work with a telescope of small aperture and very long focal length and still get a large bright solar image. Thus, one of the telescopes used to observe the sun on Mount Wilson is built in the form of a tower having a 12-inch lens at the top with a focal length of 150 feet, which gives an image of the sun 17 inches in diameter. For fainter objects, such as the moon and planets, we need a telescope with a larger aperture and enough focal length to obtain the magnification we desire, but not so long as to weaken the image unduly. It is interesting to note that we can get the same brightness of image with a small telescope as with a large one if we change the focal length accordingly. Consider two telescopes, one with a lens 5 inches in diameter and of 5 feet focal length, another with a lens 10 inches in diameter and of 10 feet focal length. The light-gathering power of the two lenses is in the proportion of $10^2/5^2$ or 100/25 or 4. That is, the 10-inch lens gathers four times as much light as the 5-inch lens. But its focal length is twice as great, so that it spreads the light over four times as large an area, making the amount of light per square inch the same. You might ask what advantage there is in using a larger lens. The advantage, of course, is that while the image we get is the same brightness as the one formed with the 5-inch lens, it is also larger. We could get an image of this size with the 5-inch lens by increasing its focal length, but the image might be so faint as to be useless for our purpose. A telescope of moderate aperture may be suitable for photographing rather bright objects such as the moon and planets but unsuitable for very faint extended objects such as the nebulae. To photograph these faint objects a very long exposure time would be needed to build up an image on the sensitive emulsion—so long that it might be impractical to attempt it. For this reason the 200-inch telescope is used almost entirely on faint objects such as the nebulae; they can hardly be studied with telescopes of smaller aperture.

▶ How is magnification obtained in a telescope?

Magnification in a telescope is secured by looking at the image formed by the lens or mirror with an eyepiece which acts as a magnifying glass. The magnification depends upon the focal length of the lens or mirror, divided by the focal length of the eyepiece. Suppose that the focal length of the lens on a telescope is 20 feet (240 inches) and we use an eyepiece of 1-inch focal length. This combination would give a magnification of 240 times. It would make the moon appear as if it were at an optical distance of 1000 miles, since the distance of the moon from the earth is 240,000 miles. We can change the magnification either by using another lens of longer focal length, or by using an eyepiece of shorter focal length. But the lens in the end of a telescope is a very expensive piece of glass; practically all the expense of a telescope is in its lens or mirror. It is much cheaper, therefore, to change the eyepiece, which costs only a few dollars. Thus by using an eyepiece of sufficiently short focal length we can obtain almost any magnification we wish. In practice, however, it is seldom of advantage to use an eyepiece that gives a magnification of more than a thousand times. This limit is determined by what astronomers refer to as the "seeing." The atmosphere is continually disturbed by rising and descending currents of air, which keep the atmosphere stirred up and which produce the "twinkling" of the stars. This effect may be pleasant to the eye, but in the telescope it is greatly magnified, so that a star seems to be jerking about wildly. Planets and the moon do not twinkle; instead their images look blurred and unsteady, like pebbles seen through running water or landscape viewed through heated air rising from a fire. An eyepiece magnifies both the moon and the unsteadiness that means poor seeing until a point is reached at which further magnification blurs the image so badly there is no use attempting it.

▶ *Can a small telescope magnify as much as a large one?*

By using a short-focus eyepiece, a small telescope can be made to magnify as much as a larger one. For example, we can easily get a magnification of a thousand times with a 10-inch telescope; as we have seen, that is as much as is practicable to use with the very largest. Thus, so far as magnification alone is concerned, there is no advantage in using a very large telescope. But a large telescope does have an advantage over a small one in resolution or power of definition. A large telescope will show finer detail than a smaller one. It might seem that we could separate finer and finer detail simply by using more magnification, but this is not true. To demonstrate this, suppose that we took a photograph of the foliage on a tree. In some places the foliage is bunched together on the picture so that the individual leaves cannot be discerned. Regardless of how much we enlarge the picture, we can never separate the foliage into individual leaves. Something of the same sort is true of a telescope. If two stars are sufficiently close together in a certain telescope, no amount of magnification will separate them into individual stars. To do this we must use a telescope with a larger aperture, which will make the images of the stars appear smaller; only then can we resolve them, or split them into two stars instead of one blurred, elongated image.

26

▶ *Which is better: refractor or reflector?*

Both instruments have advantages and disadvantages; the choice must often depend upon the purpose for which the telescope is to be used. A refractor has one serious disadvantage: it is impossible to bring light of every color to the same focus. This can be partly overcome by making the objective (lens system) of two different kinds of glass that bend the light in slightly different ways instead of using a single lens. By a suitable choice of glass the yellow and green rays to which the eye is most sensitive can be brought into a common focus. But the correction is never perfect; the image will be surrounded by a red-violet ring of light that is out of focus. All rays are *reflected* equally, so this problem does not exist with a reflector.

It is often claimed that a refractor gives better definition than a reflector of the same size. This is because an error in polishing a mirror is more serious than the same error in polishing a lens. Telescope mirrors can now be ground so perfectly, however, that there is not much difference between the two. At least, makers of the best reflecting telescopes deny there is any difference.

So far as size goes, the advantage is heavily in favor of the reflector. A good lens requires the best optical glass, clear and without bubbles, whereas ordinary glass filled with bubbles may be used for a reflector. In a refractor, also, several surfaces have to be ground to the proper shape, compared with only one in a reflector. Also, reflectors can be made much larger than refractors for a fraction of the cost. The advantage today would seem to be definitely with the reflector.

▶ *What are some points to remember
in buying a telescope?*

Astronomers are often asked to give advice on buying a small telescope, something they usually avoid if possible. It is hard to give advice about a telescope without knowing how much money the purchaser wishes to put into it or how much he wants to accomplish with it. The best general procedure for a novice purchasing his first telescope is to get an experienced person in whom he has confidence to examine the instrument for him, if possible.

27

Most people who purchase a telescope do so because their interest in the heavens has been awakened, and they desire to see with their own eyes some of the wonders in the sky they have read about in books. To see some of these objects a telescope with an aperture of at least 3 inches is desirable. With such a telescope one may easily view the craters on the moon, the rings of Saturn, the phases of Venus, and the four large moons of Jupiter. One may also obtain a good view of certain star clusters, nebulae, and double stars. Mars is a very difficult object and will probably show only a reddish disk in a telescope of this size. Refractors are usually more expensive than reflectors of the same size; since small reflectors of very high quality are now available, they are probably better instruments to purchase, unless one has an opportunity to make an exceptionally good buy in a refractor.

Any purchaser naturally wants a telescope that gives a sharp image of a distant object. If you are buying a refractor, be especially careful to see that it is properly corrected for color. (This is a problem that does not arise in a reflector, since a mirror brings rays of all colors to a common focus. If objects in a refractor show a conspicuous purple halo the lens has not been suitably corrected and should be rejected. Since it is impossible to correct a lens completely for color, a refracting telescope will usually show objects with a bluish tinge. This is often especially noticeable when viewing the craters on the moon.

Venus is too difficult an object to use in testing a telescope and Saturn probably too easy; an object like Jupiter is a good one. The planet should appear as a sharply defined oval disk in the field of view with cloud belts extending across it. The images of the satellites should appear as nearly round points of light; they should not be distorted into lines, or have flares extending from them. Of course, if you test your telescope on a night when the air is unsteady so that the seeing is bad, it will be hard to form a dependable opinion concerning the quality of the lens or mirror in question. For this reason, if possible try the telescope out on several nights.

A good secondhand telescope can often be picked up at considerably less cost than a new one. Remember that a telescope does not depreciate with age, as an automobile does. But never let yourself be pressured into buying a telescope in a hurry! In particular, the lens in a telescope does not deteriorate with age, although it may need cleaning. Telescope mirrors used to be coated with silver, which corroded so rapidly that in large observatories they were usually recoated regularly once a year. Now mirrors are coated with aluminum, which gives a bright coat that lasts for many years. They may be aluminized again at moderate cost. Anyone who plans to buy a telescope should visit several dealers and compare instruments and prices. The beginner will do well to start with a small instrument (of around 3 inches' aperture) before he puts several hundred dollars into a larger one.

One point often overlooked in buying a telescope is the mounting. Is it firm and free from wobble and flexure? Is it easy to move the instrument around and point the telescope in different directions? Will it remain pointed in a particular direction once it is set there or does it have some "give" to it? No matter how good a lens or mirror may be it is useless unless it is properly mounted so that the viewer can take observations through it in comfort and without fear that his instrument is in danger of collapsing on him at any moment.

3 ▶ THE MOON
AND ITS SURFACE FEATURES

▶ *How far away is the moon?*

The moon is the only planet which is close enough to the earth to appear as a disk to our unaided eyes. The other planets, except Pluto, appear as distinct disks through a telescope, but to the eye they simply look like stars. If the moon were at the distance of Mars when it is closest to the earth, it would appear as a star of moderate brightness. At the distance of Jupiter it would be just on the limit of visibility. But the moon is near enough so that it shows us a disk on which markings are easily visible. The distance of the moon ranges from 221,000 miles when closest to the earth to 253,000 miles when farthest away; average distance is 240,000 miles. Most astronomical distances are so immense that they mean nothing to us. Even the distance of the nearer planets (50 million miles or so) is difficult to grasp, since it is so far outside our experience. Here I will let you in on a little secret: Astronomers can't conceive of these distances any better than other people. The difference is that they don't make the mistake of trying.

The moon is close enough, however, for us to form some idea of its distance in space. The distance across the United States is about 3000 miles. Such a flight can be made in less than half a day. Forty round trips across the United States would equal the distance to the moon. There must be many pilots and airline stewardesses who have traveled much farther than the distance to the moon. The distance around the earth is 25,000 miles; flying around the earth ten times would be the same as traveling the distance to the moon. Or you can think of the distance to the moon in terms of the size of the earth, which is about 8000 miles through from pole to pole. So if you had thirty earths stacked on top of one another they

30

would just reach to the moon. Since we all have a general idea of the size of the earth on which we live, it is not too hard to think of thirty earths extending off into space—growing smaller and smaller until they finally reach the moon.

▶ *How big is the moon, and how heavy?*

The moon is about a thousand miles (1080, to be exact) from center to surface, or 2160 miles all the way through. Figure 13 shows the relative sizes of those planets similar in size to the earth, which include the moon, earth, Mercury, Venus, and Mars. These are often called the terrestrial planets.

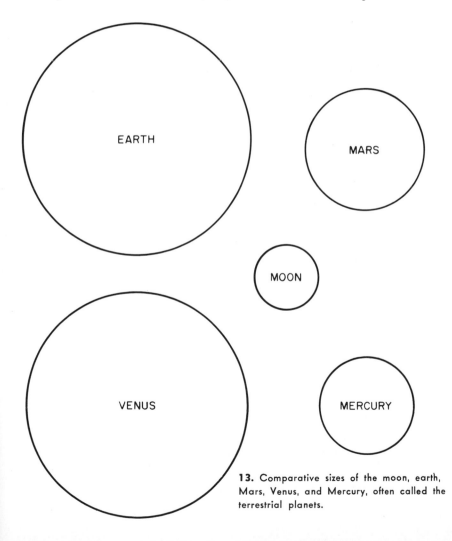

13. Comparative sizes of the moon, earth, Mars, Venus, and Mercury, often called the terrestrial planets.

The moon is so large in relation to the earth that from outer space the earth and moon together would look like a twin planet.

Although the moon is one quarter the size of the earth in diameter, it is only about 1 per cent (1/81) as massive as the earth. If you put the earth and moon on opposite ends of a seesaw, the moon would have to be 81 times as far from the center as the earth to make the two planets balance. It would be like trying to set up a balance between a kitten and a St. Bernard. Because of its lower mass the moon is also much less dense than the earth. The mass of a body is the total amount of matter contained within it. The density of a body is the amount of mass per unit volume. Thus a pound of cotton and a pound of iron both have the same mass. But the density of the iron is much greater.

If you could stir up the earth and the moon until they were uniformly mixed from center to surface, a sample of the moon would weigh only 60 per cent as much as a sample of the earth. This indicates that the moon has no heavy iron core such as that which gives the earth its high density (5.5 times that of water). The average density of the moon is 3.3 times that of water, about the same as the basic rocks just below the thin granite surface layer of the earth.

▶ *What makes the moon rise and set?*

The moon rises and sets for the same reason all the other objects in the sky do—because of the rotation of the earth on its axis from west to east. As the rotation of the earth carries us toward the east, everything in the sky seems to move toward the west, just as objects in the landscape viewed from a train window seem to be moving in the opposite direction from the train. Figure 14 shows the sun, photographed during the morning at intervals of about twenty minutes. The earth rotated a little between exposures, carrying the photographer with his camera farther around toward the sun, so that it appears to be moving upward in the sky. At noon the rotation of the earth would have carried him almost under the sun; after that the sun would have seemed to set as the earth's rotation carried the camera out from below the sun.

The moon shares with all the other bodies in the sky this general

14. Successive images of the sun, taken by making an exposure at intervals of about twenty minutes. As the earth turns eastward the sun appears to rise and to move toward the west.

motion toward the west. But the moon also has an eastward motion, a fact you can easily verify when it happens to be near a bright star. Notice the position of the moon in relation to the star at, say, eight o'clock in the evening. Then check on it again at ten o'clock. You will find the moon has moved eastward from the star about twice its diameter because of its orbital revolution around the earth. During the course of a day the moon will have moved a distance equal to about twenty-four times its width, or about 12 degrees in the sky. This means that the moon will rise a little later in the sky each night. Suppose that on a certain night the moon rises at the same time a bright star does. The next night the moon will be twenty-four times its width *east* of the star. The star will rise at about the same time; but you will have to wait about 50 minutes, until the earth has turned through the distance the moon has moved eastward, before you will see the moon rise.

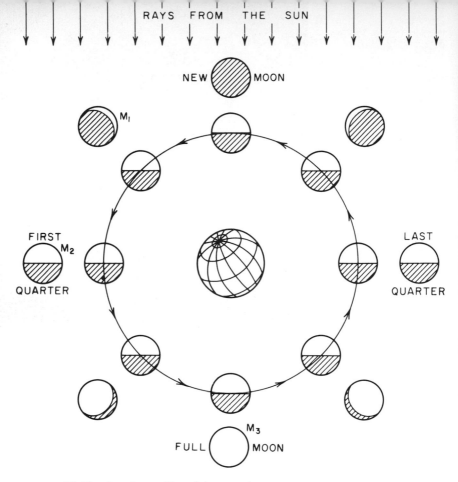

RAYS FROM THE SUN

NEW MOON

M₁

FIRST QUARTER   M₂

LAST QUARTER

FULL MOON   M₃

15. The changing position of the moon in relation to the earth and sun produces its phases. Figures in outer circle show appearance of moon at different positions.

▶ *Why is the appearance of the moon always changing?*

The moon's appearance changes because its position in relation to the earth and sun is always changing. Look at Figure 15, which shows the disks of the sun and moon somewhat as they appear to an observer on the earth. (It is impossible to represent the sun and moon accurately in a diagram since the sun is 400 times as far from the earth as the moon is, but a diagram will give the general idea.)

34

16. Dark areas on the face of our satellite make up the familiar features of the "man in the moon."

The observer first sees the moon as a thin crescent in the western sky after sunset, as at M_1. As the moon progresses eastward in its orbit the crescent grows until (at M_2) it has moved a quarter of the distance around from the sun in its orbit, and we see just half the disk of the moon that is turned toward the earth. As the moon continues in its orbit we see more than half its disk, until finally (at M_3) the whole daylight side of the moon is turned in our direction. The moon then goes through its phases in reverse order until it comes around to new moon again.

▶ *What makes up the face of the "man in the moon"?*

The markings that make up the rather blurred features of the "man in the moon" are simply regions on the lunar surface that are darker than the rest. Early astronomers, such as Galileo and others who followed him, were unable to see these dark areas distinctly with their small, imperfect telescopes, so they called them *maria* (seas) because they thought them actual bodies of water. Today we know that the moon has no air or water on its surface, but the names given to these dark areas have been retained, and we still speak of the moon's Sea of Serenity, Sea of Tranquility, and Ocean of Storms.

▶ What is moonlight?

Moonlight is really sunlight reflected to the earth from the surface of the moon. Moonlight often seems very bright to us. Looking over a landscape illuminated by the full moon, we exclaim, "Why, it's as bright as day!" Actual measurements show that moonlight is only 1/400,000 as bright as sunlight. Owing to its irregular surface, the moon makes a poor reflector, reflecting only about 7 per cent of the sun's light that falls on it. The full moon looks bright in the sky at night, but when we see it during the day while the sun is shining, its disk is so faint that we might easily mistake it for a patch of cloud.

We might naturally assume that when the moon is at the quarter phase, so that we see half the disk illuminated, we would get half as much light as we get at full moon. Actually we get only one ninth as much. The reason is that much of the moon's surface is covered by the shadows of mountains and craters and therefore considerably less than half the disk is illuminated by the sun. The moon is a little brighter at first quarter than at last quarter since some parts of the moon reflect better than others.

We also receive more moonlight in winter than in summer. The full moon is always just opposite the sun in the sky. When it is winter in the northern hemisphere, the sun is far to the south and low in the sky; the full moon is far to the north and thus high in the sky. Not only is the full moon higher in the sky but we also get more hours of moonlight, as if to make up for the lack of sunshine.

▶ What is meant by "the new moon
in the old moon's arms"?

This effect is caused by reflected light from the earth falling on the moon and being reflected back to earth again. The effect is most evident when the moon is at the crescent phase. Then we see the bright disk of the crescent moon that is illuminated by the sun. But the night side of the moon also shows as a bluish disk. The cause of the effect is shown in Figure 17, in which we are supposed to be looking down on the earth and moon in space. The side of the moon drawn in heavy solid line is turned toward the earth. An observer on the earth sees only a small part of the illuminated surface; to him the moon appears a crescent. At the same time, seen from the moon, the earth is nearly full. It is the light from the nearly full earth shining on the moon and dimly lighting its surface that sometimes gives the disk of the moon its dim bluish tint when it is at the crescent phase. In other words, it is earthshine on the moon that produces the effect called "the new moon in the old moon's arms."

Sir William Herschel, the great eighteenth-century English astronomer who discovered the planet Uranus, once claimed to have

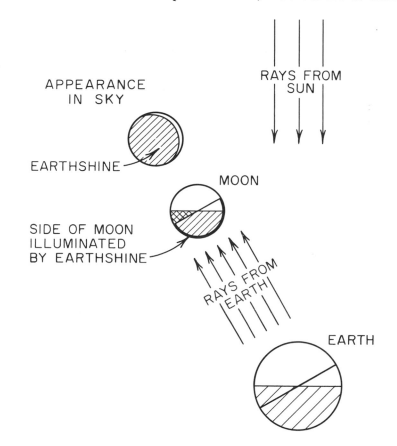

APPEARANCE
IN SKY

RAYS FROM
SUN

EARTHSHINE

MOON

SIDE OF MOON
ILLUMINATED
BY EARTHSHINE

RAYS FROM
EARTH

EARTH

Light reflected from the earth onto the dark side of the moon produces the faint illumination called the "new moon he old man's arms."

seen a lunar volcano in eruption on the night side of the disk. What he undoubtedly observed was a bright crater such as Aristarchus illuminated by earthshine.

▶ *If the moon rotates, why does it always keep the same side turned toward the earth?*

If the moon turned around once every couple of days, we would be able to see all sides of it. But the moon rotates on its

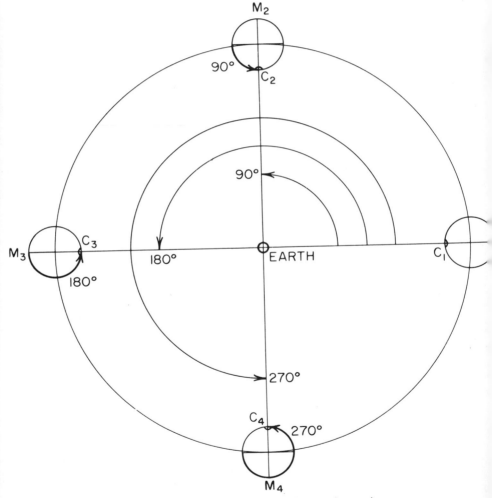

18. Why the moon always keeps the same side turned toward the earth: when the moon revolves through a quarter of a revolution it must also rotate through a quarter of a revolution and so on.

axis at *exactly* the same rate it revolves around the earth. And that is what causes all the confusion.

Suppose first that the moon is at M_1 and that there is a large crater at C_1 on the side turned toward the earth, so that we will have a way of distinguishing one side from the other. In relation to the fixed stars, the crater lies in the direction Earth C_1M_1 at this position. The moon moves along in its orbit to M_2, *keeping the same side always turned toward the earth*. The moon has now moved one quarter of the way around in its orbit. Originally the direction of the crater was along the line Earth C_1M_1. At M_2 if the direction of the crater is still earthward then the moon *must* have rotated a quarter of a turn around to C_2, for if the moon had *not* rotated it would still be in the direction of the line Earth C_1M_1. The moon continues on for another quarter of a revolution until it is halfway around in its orbit to M_3. But to keep the same side turned toward the earth the moon must again have made a quarter turn until the crater is facing the earth at C_3. Finally the moon comes around to its original position; the crater is again at C_1 and still turned toward the earth. The moon has made a complete revolution in its orbit and has also made a complete turn on its axis.

While the moon rotates at a steady rate on its *axis,* it does not revolve at a steady rate in its orbit. As a result, during the course of the month the moon's rate of revolution does not quite keep in step with its rate of rotation. The moon moves fastest when it is nearest the earth, slowest when farthest away. Suppose the moon is closest to the earth at M_1, and farthest away at M_3. It will move through a quarter of a revolution in slightly less than a quarter of a month, going from M_1 to M_2, so that the moon will not have time to turn through quite a quarter of a rotation. Thus at M_2 the crater (C) would not appear quite as near the center of the disk as it did at M_1. Similarly, we would be able to see a little more of the peak at P_1 than we did at M_1, but the peak at P_2 would be completely out of sight. At M_3 the situation would be the same as at M_1. But it takes a little *more* than a quarter of a month for the moon to move from M_3 to M_4, so that the moon would have time to make slightly more than a quarter of a turn. The result is that at M_4 the crater would appear slightly to the right of the center of the disk, and the peak at P_2 would be brought

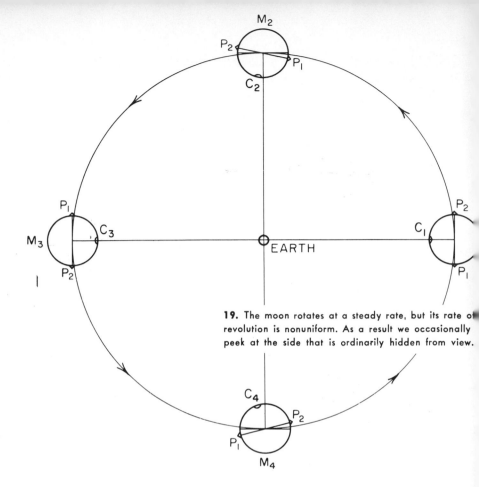

19. The moon rotates at a steady rate, but its rate of revolution is nonuniform. As a result we occasionally peek at the side that is ordinarily hidden from view.

into view while the peak at P_1 would be just out of sight. At M_1 everything is lined up again, as it was in the beginning. Thus it is incorrect to say that we always see the same side of the moon. As the result of its nonuniform rate of revolution, we alternately see a little more of the moon's surface than we should if its rate of rotation coincided precisely with its rate of revolution.

This is what is called one of the *librations* of the moon, a formidable-sounding term that comes from the word *libra* (a balance); it is descriptive of the swaying back and forth of a set of scales. As a result of the librations of the moon we can see altogether 59 per cent of its surface; there is 41 per cent that we never see. People have often wondered what the back side of the moon

40

looks like. From the first photographs of it, it does not look essentially different from the side always visible to us.

▶ How does the moon move in relation to the earth?

.Suppose that you were in a space ship about a million miles above the north pole of the earth, moving at the same speed and in the same direction as the earth in its path around the sun. In the course of time, by measuring the position of the moon in relation to the earth, you would find that it is revolving around the earth in a nearly circular orbit. Figure 20 shows the position of the earth at E_1 in its orbit and the moon at M_1 when it is directly in line with the sun. There are some stars in the direction

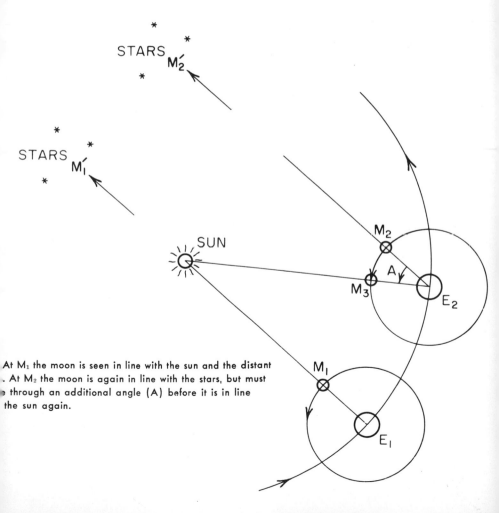

At M_1 the moon is seen in line with the sun and the distant
. At M_2 the moon is again in line with the stars, but must
through an additional angle (A) before it is in line
the sun again.

E_1S, and we will suppose that the moon is visible among them at M_1'.

After 27.3 days the earth has moved on around the sun until it is at E_2 and the moon again appears among the same stars at the same position it did before, at M_2'. (The stars are at such an immense distance that their *direction* in space remains the same. It is unaffected by the little distance the earth moves in its orbit.) But now the moon is not in line with the sun as it was at E_1M_1. That is, because of the revolution of the earth around the sun, the moon will have to move on through an additional distance equal to the angle A to M_3 before it is seen in the same direction as the sun again.

The true time of revolution of the moon around the earth is the time it takes to go from a certain position in relation to the stars back to that same position again. This is called the sidereal or star month, and its length is about 27.3 days (27 days 7 hours 44 minutes 2.78 seconds, exactly). The time required for the moon to travel from a certain position in relation to the sun back to that same position again, as from new moon to new moon or full moon to full moon, is about two days longer, averaging 29.5 days. That is, after the moon comes in line with the same stars as before, it must still travel another 2 days to catch up with the sun again. This interval of 29.5 days is called the synodic month.

▶ *How does the moon move in relation to the sun?*

If you did not move with the earth, but tried to observe the path of the earth and moon as they swing together around the sun, you would find that the path of the moon looks entirely different from the way it did before. It does not seem to be revolving around the earth at all. If the earth and moon left vapor trails behind them, as a jet plane does, their trails would be so intertwined as to be almost indistinguishable. The moon not only revolves around the earth, it also revolves around the sun. And its motion around the sun is on such a large scale that the little distance the moon keeps from the earth seems trivial by comparison. The interesting feature about the moon's path is that it is *always concave toward the sun*. Even at new moon, the moon's path is

42

rounded inward toward the sun, never outward as might be supposed.

▶ *What is the nature of the maria of the moon?*

To Galileo and the astronomers of his time there was no mystery about the dark regions that form the familiar face of the "man in the moon." In their telescopes they appeared as dark regions not greatly different from the way they appear to the unaided eye. They *looked like* seas and oceans. So the astronomers decided they *were* seas and oceans and accordingly named them *maria*. Today, after three centuries, the nature of these large dark

21. The moon age 11 days. The dark areas are the so-called "seas." The bright streaks radiating from some of the craters are rays.

22. The dark smooth expanse here is the Mare Imbrium, believed to have been caused by the impact of a meteorite or asteroid.

regions still eludes us, although we do know that they are not bodies of water.

In contrast to the pockmarked surface around them, the maria are relatively smooth. They are not free of craters but craters are certainly much less frequent on the vast plains of the maria than on the regions surrounding them. The maria really do remind us strongly of seas. Many adjoining craters have seaward walls that are lower than the landward, as if they were partially submerged. Also, most of the maria show "ghost" craters, which give the impression of craters totally or partially submerged beneath the floor of the plain. There are also many ridges on the floor of the maria which make us think of the crest of a long, smooth wave that solidified before it reached the shoreline.

Because the surface of the maria so strongly suggest a liquid in motion, it has been generally supposed that they are the result of extensive lava flows. This has led to the idea proposed by Ralph B. Baldwin that the lava was released from the interior of the moon through fissures caused by meteoritic impact. Baldwin estimates that Mare Imbrium had its origin in the impact of a meteorite of nickel–iron about 10 miles in diameter that struck with a velocity of 20 miles per second. The meteorite disappeared beneath the surface, leaving only a small sharp hole to mark its passage. There was a moment of calm. Then "a great section of the crust, several hundreds of miles across, domed up, split rapidly and radially from the central point. Surface layers peeled back on themselves like the opening of a gigantic flower, followed quickly by a stamen of dust and fragments spreading rapidly in all directions without the roiling turbulence imparted by an atmosphere."

After the impact there was a tremendous rebound. A great segment of the crust rose upward, forming a mound which became fixed as a structural dome. Then the great central block of the dome began to settle. As it sank, huge columns of lava welled and bubbled up, filling the hollow space left by the sinking dome. The lava spread rapidly over the face of the moon, flowing out among the surrounding mountains to produce Mare Nubium and Oceanus Procellarum to the east, and Mare Serenitatis, Mare Tranquilitatis, and Mare Foecunditatis on the west. Thus practically all of the seas on the moon, according to Baldwin's hypothesis, were created in one grand splash.

Harold C. Urey has objected that if there was lava originally below the surface of the Mare Imbrium before it was struck by the giant meteorite or asteroid, then the surface material must have been heavier than the molten region beneath it. Why did it not sink, or why did the lava not flow up through cracks in the surface? Urey believes that the lava was formed from the meteorite itself, which formed a molten pool upon impact. The lava spread out, not only forming Mare Imbrium and other neighboring seas, but dropping the material that produced the mountains in this area.

Thomas Gold, on the other hand, does not believe in the lava-flow hypothesis at all. He assumes that the maria originated the same way the craters did, by explosions resulting from meteoritic impact, only on a vastly larger scale than the craters. Later the floors of these vast craters or walled plains became covered with dust from the surrounding highlands. This dust may have originated from the impact of meteorites or micrometeorites (particles only a few millionths of an inch long) on the rough surface and, if there was a thin atmosphere present, could have been carried and deposited in the lower maria. In this way the maria eventually became filled to a depth of possibly a thousand feet in a period that may have extended over three thousand million years, or at the rate of about one inch in 250,000 years. The darker color of the maria may be the result of radiation due to ultraviolet light, soft X rays from the sun, and cosmic rays. The dust which had traveled the farthest and been in transit the longest would be darkened the most. The lighter color of the highlands is due to the fact that they lost material that settled in the maria.

Most astronomers are willing to admit a dust layer of possibly an inch or so in depth but one a thousand feet deep is something else again. It would indicate that travelers to the moon may have to wear snowshoes even though the temperature of the surface is up around the boiling point of water.

▶ *How do we know that the moon has no atmosphere?*

It is easy to tell that the moon does not have an atmosphere comparable to that of the earth. We could probably tell this much simply by keeping a close watch on the disk of the moon with the unaided eye. The features on the disk of the moon are never obscured by clouds or haze or storms such as sweep over the surface of the earth. With a large telescope we can scan the moon's surface in minute detail in search of an atmosphere. But even to the very edge of the moon, where the atmosphere would be thickest if any existed, the surface features are as sharp as at the center. There is no twilight along the region between night and day. The shadows always stand out sharp and well defined.

A more sensitive test for an atmosphere is provided when the moon occults a star. The moon is moving eastward in its orbit against the background of the fixed stars. Occasionally the disk of the moon passes in front of a star, blotting it out. If the moon had an atmosphere, the star would fade out gradually, wavering and changing color as the beam from the star passed through successively deeper layers of the lunar atmosphere. Instead, the star vanishes with startling abruptness. It is there one instant and gone the next. The star reappears in the same abrupt manner. The test is very sensitive. It has been estimated that if the moon had an atmosphere only one ten-thousandth as dense as the atmosphere of the earth it could readily be detected by the occultation of a star.

▶ *What has happened to the atmosphere of the moon?*

It is possible that millions of years ago the moon had an atmosphere. To understand why the moon has no atmosphere today we first have to form some picture of how the gas particles of the atmosphere behave. We can think of the molecules of a gas as hard, tiny spheres that are in continual motion, colliding with one another and bouncing apart like billiard balls. (It is the force of these collisions with the walls of a tire that keeps the tire inflated.) The average speed with which a molecule moves depends upon its mass and the temperature of the gas. The lighter molecules move faster than the heavier ones. The speed of all the molecules increases as the temperature rises.

Imagine a group of people of various sizes and ages struggling to get out of a crowded room. Those near the center will have little chance of escaping. They can go only a few feet before their way is blocked by others going in the opposite direction. In fact, they are continually jostled and knocked about so that they are unable to go very far in any direction. But occasionally, near the edge of the crowd an agile person sees an opening and is able to dart outside and escape through an exit before someone blocks his way.

The molecules in the atmosphere of a planet are in somewhat the same situation. The molecules in the lower, denser part of an atmosphere will have very little chance of escaping from the planet into outer space. Suppose a molecule does start moving away from the surface of a planet—in a fraction of a second it will have undergone a series of collisions with other molecules that will turn it back again. In fact, the sky above it is filled with a dense cloud of molecules flying about in all directions; the chance of penetrating any distance through them is hopeless. Not until we reach the uppermost limits of the atmosphere do the molecules thin out enough so that one has a chance of escaping forever into outer space.

For a molecule to fly away from a planet, never to return, it must be moving with a certain minimum velocity, called appropriately the *velocity of escape*. At an altitude of 200 miles above the earth the velocity of escape is about 6.8 miles (or approximately 36,000 ft) per second. As we go upward in the atmosphere the temperature falls at first, so that at an altitude of a few hundred miles it is below freezing. But at great altitudes, due to the action of ultraviolet light from the sun upon the gas particles, the temperature rises to around 4000° F. Even at this temperature the average speed of a hydrogen molecule would be only 3.4 miles per second, much below the velocity of escape. But remember that this is the *average* velocity of the molecules. Some will be moving much more slowly than the average. Others will be moving as fast or faster than the velocity of escape, and unless they suffer a collision that turns them back they will fly away from the planet, never to return.

The velocity of escape differs widely among the planets, depending upon their size and mass. A large planet of small mass would have a low velocity of escape. A small but massive planet would have a high velocity of escape. Thus, although Saturn is ninety-five times as massive as the earth, its mass is distended through such a large volume that velocity of escape is only about three times that required for the earth. Here is a table that gives the velocity of escape for the principal bodies of the solar system:

Planet	Velocity of Escape
Sun	383 miles/sec
Mercury	2.7
Venus	6.5
Earth	7.0
Moon	1.5
Mars	3.2
Jupiter	38.
Saturn	23.
Uranus	14.
Neptune	16.
Pluto *	?

* The size and mass of Pluto are so uncertain it is impossible to calculate a reliable value for its velocity of escape.

. It can be shown that if the velocity of escape is four times larger than the average velocity of the molecules, the molecules will all be lost to the planet in a matter of a thousand years. If the velocity of escape is five times the average velocity of the molecules, they will not disappear for a billion years. And if it is six times as large, the planet will be able to hang onto its atmosphere practically forever. Thus the earth is massive enough to retain all gases except the very lightest, hydrogen and helium. But the velocity of escape is so low for the moon (the lowest in the table) that it could only retain a few heavy gases.

▶ What are lunar craters?

The first time you see the lunar craters there is not likely to be much doubt in your mind as to what they are. They are volcanoes! This is especially true if you see them about first quarter when they are in deep shadow along the line where the sun is rising. These deep dark holes with their high surrounding rims can't be anything else. Lunar craters and mountains have a cold, sculptured look like that of icing on a cake. What an inferno the surface of the moon must have been when they all were spouting fire!

The early astronomers with their small and imperfect telescopes also took it for granted that the lunar craters were volcanoes and seemed to have little inclination to question their belief. The idea

23. Crescent moon and Saturn.

that the craters might have had an entirely different origin was slow in coming. Only during the last century, in fact, has the volcanic hypothesis been seriously challenged. Actually, the lunar craters bear no resemblance to terrestrial volcanoes. Volcanoes on earth are cone-shaped structures that slope up to a small opening at the top. The lunar craters, on the other hand, have mostly the shape of shallow cups or saucers. When the craters are in shadow they look like deep pits surrounded by high walls. This is because light and shade on the moon stand out in such strong contrast. There is no air to scatter the sun's rays as on the earth, where the shadows are soft with diffused light. On the moon, shadows are sharp and black. Therefore when the floor of a crater is in shadow it seems much deeper than it is, and the long shadows cast by the crater rim give a false impression of height. Not until we see the moon's craters under flat lighting near the full phase do we begin to realize how shallow they really are. In fact, if we stood in the center of some of the largest craters we would hardly be aware of the crater wall—it would be mostly below the horizon.

All sorts of explanations of the origin of lunar craters have been advanced by those who do not believe in the volcanic hypothesis, some of them so fantastic as to be scarcely worthy of mention. One of the earliest was suggested in 1667 by Robert Hooke. He held that the lunar craters originated from tremendous gas bubbles that rose through the hot, sticky lunar crust and burst, throwing up a mass of debris that formed the crater rim—an idea that might occur to anyone watching the bubbles thrown up in a pan of boiling fudge. Unfortunately for Hooke's theory, bubbles 100 miles across are out of the question.

Equally fantastic is the idea that the moon's surface is covered by a layer of ice several thousand feet deep. There are pockets underneath where the internal heat of the moon gets through, melting the ice in spots upon the surface, forming pools of water. Since vacuum conditions prevail over the surface of the moon, the water would quickly evaporate and be deposited around the rim of the pool in the form of a crater. We need only say that radiation from the surface of the moon directly under the sun has been measured and found to correspond to the temperature of boiling water, which hardly fits in with the thick-covering-of-ice explanation.

The idea that really takes the prize makes the craters limestone formations, like coral atolls on earth. On this basis, the moon's surface was once an ancient ocean bed and the craters built by accretion from marine organisms. The total lack of evidence for erosion due to water on the moon should be enough to dispose of the coral-atoll theory for all time.

▶ *How do most astronomers today believe the lunar craters were formed?*

It seems strange that, when the moon is so close to us, we still know so little about how its surface features were formed. We can examine these features in detail. Under good atmospheric conditions a telescope will bring the moon within

51

an optical distance of some 240 miles. Yet only recently have we been able to speak about their origin with any assurance.

The first person who seems to have been on the right track was a German astronomer named Franz von Paula Gruithuisen, who in 1822 suggested that the craters were formed by the impact of huge meteorites striking the surface of the moon when it was in a plastic condition. The idea was revived in 1873 by the English astronomer R. A. Proctor, who held that the craters were simply

24. Southern portion of the moon photographed at last quarter. The surface is thickly studded with craters in this area.

gouged out of the lunar crust by mechanical impact. A tolerably good imitation of a lunar crater can be formed by hurling a stone into soft mud.

What the earlier astronomers failed to realize was that it is not necessary for the surface of the moon to have been in a plastic condition. A hard surface would have done just as well. A meteorite may strike the surface with a velocity anywhere from 5 to 50 miles per second. Remember that the moon has no atmosphere to break the fall. The result of an impact with a velocity of several miles per second is not merely to gouge a hole in the surface. The result is an explosion!

An American astronomer, Ralph B. Baldwin, has figured the consequences of such a lunar impact in great detail. The collision would occur with such violence that the portion of the meteorite in contact with the surface would be vaporized, an effect essentially the same as a bomb explosion. Thus it would be possible for meteorites to blow gigantic holes in the hard crust—much larger than the bodies that produced them. Baldwin has given a vivid picture of what happens when a meteorite strikes the moon. It plunges beneath the surface, pushing ahead of it a plug of compressed rock and air. Little heat is generated immediately upon impact, since heat is due to the random motions of the molecules of the rock, and the meteorite at first is moving faster than the shock waves it sets up. When the speed of motion drops below that of the waves running through the material, the mass is soon stopped. By now the meteorite is sitting on top of a tremendously compressed, tremendously hot plug of matter. The result is a violent explosion. Material is blown away, upward at first, then more toward the sides. In this way the crater is assumed to have been formed.

What makes the idea of craters formed by meteoritic explosion especially convincing is the fact that we can tie them in with bomb craters on the earth. Measurements made of terrestrial bomb craters have shown a definite relationship between their width and depth. The same sort of relationship has been found to hold for the craters on the moon. In fact, there is no difference between the two.

Thus, according to current ideas, the lunar craters are really *explosion pits,* ranging in size from mere specks a few thousand feet across to Clavius, 146 miles in diameter. There are some

53

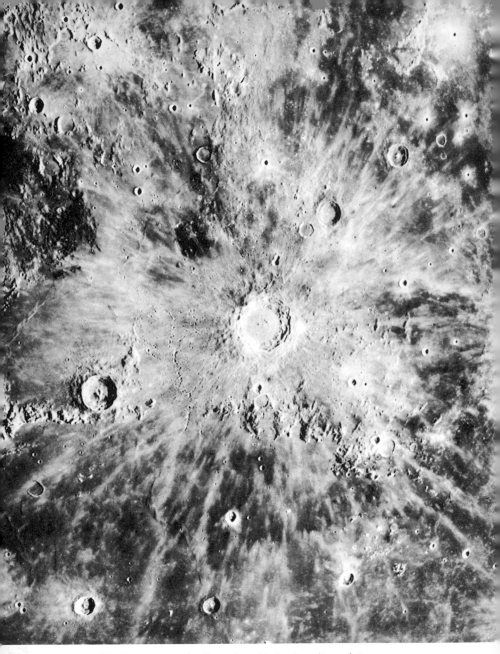

25. The great crater Copernicus. Notice long lines of tiny craterlets nearby.

craterlets on the moon which occur in long chains like postholes dug for a fence. It is hard to see how these could have been produced by meteorites landing in such a regular linelike fashion. These craterlets may indeed be some kind of volcanic blowholes through which gases were released from beneath the moon's crust. Such blowhole craters are particularly prominent near the great crater Copernicus.

▶ How did the moon's craters get their names?

Most of the craters on the moon have been named for scientists and philosophers who lived in ancient and medieval times. The custom of applying personal names to the lunar formations began in 1645 with Langrenus of Brussels, who published the first map of the moon. He named the largest ocean after his patron, Philip IV of Spain, and awarded other prominent features to various members of the royal family. The rest were named for astronomers of his own day.

Most of this was changed when Giovanni Battista Riccioli of Bologna (1598–1671) completed his great lunar map six years later. He promptly cast out the members of the royal Spanish household and replaced them with his contemporaries and ancient and medieval astronomers, putting the ancients into the northern hemisphere and the more modern ones in the southern.

In the early nineteenth century observers working with larger telescopes produced improved maps; since there were no regulations on the matter, they added names freely as fancy dictated. Since it was embarrassing to apply their own names to craters, however, selenographers named them after each other. But many had no hesitation about assuring their immortality on the moon by selecting a crater well in advance of their demise.

As more and more names were added to the maps, the surface of the moon got into such a state of hopeless nomenclatural confusion that something had to be done to straighten it out. This finally was done by the British Astronomical Association in 1939 with the issuance of a catalogue of officially named lunar formations, *Who's Who on the Moon.*

Eight craters on the moon bear the names of women. Of these, by far the largest is Catherina, in honor of the semilegendary St.

55

Catherine of Alexandria, who died a martyr's death and for whom the Catherine wheel is named. Another is named for Caroline Herschel (1750–1848), sister of the great Sir William Herschel who discovered the planet Uranus. Another woman so honored is Maria Mitchell (1818–1889), at one time director of the Vassar College Observatory. Of exceptional interest on the Pacific coast of the U.S. is the name of Catherine Wolfe Bruce (1816–1900), noted for her many gifts to astronomy, in particular the gold medal of the Astronomical Society of the Pacific.

Among distinguished American astronomers whose names appear on maps of the moon are S. W. Burnham (1838–1921), the famous double-star observer; Asaph Hall (1829–1907), who discovered the two tiny moons of Mars; Simon Newcomb (1835–1900), who investigated the origin of the asteroids and the motions and masses of Uranus and Neptune; and G. W. Ritchey, who shaped the 60-inch and 100-inch mirrors of the Mount Wilson Observatory. Among recent additions is the naming of a crater in honor of the late Russell W. Porter, who aided in the design of the 200-inch telescope, and who did much to popularize astronomy.

Two businessmen who founded large observatories have had lunar craters named for them. One is James Lick (1796–1876), who made a fortune in various California enterprises, and who is buried under the 36-inch telescope of the Lick Observatory on Mount Hamilton, California. The other is Charles T. Yerkes (1837–1905), a traction magnate who donated the funds for the Yerkes Observatory of the University of Chicago.

The size of a crater is not always in proportion to the fame of the man for whom it is named, however. Several fairly large craters bear the names of men whose work now is almost forgotten.

Since all the prominent craters are now occupied, famous astronomers of the present and future will have to be content with insignificant craters that their colleagues of two hundred years ago would have regarded with scorn. But perhaps space travel will reveal a whole new vista of giant headstones on the far side of the moon.

▶ *How long would it take to reach the moon?*

This depends entirely upon the distance from the earth to the moon when the rocket is launched, and its speed at launching. A difference in velocity of only a fraction of a mile per second at the start can make a difference of a dozen hours or more in the length of the trip. Fortunately, time is not too important in going to the moon. The main object is to get there. Just to reach the moon starting with the lowest possible speed taxes our resources to the utmost. The first man-made object to reach the moon was the Russian rocket that landed on September 13, 1959. According to Soviet reports, this consisted of an 860-pound instrument package and the 3,331-pound final stage of the rocket, both of which struck the target. Later the Soviets accomplished the still more difficult feat of sending around the moon a rocket probe which obtained a photograph of the back side which is always hidden from our view.

Once the final stage of a rocket is launched into unpowered flight, it becomes exactly the same as a meteorite in space, moving under the combined gravitational attraction of the earth, sun, and moon. The attraction of the earth is the dominating force during most of the trip. The attraction of the sun remains practically the same throughout the entire journey. The attraction of the moon is so slight that it will not cause the rocket to change course appreciably unless it is within a few thousand miles of the lunar surface. But the attraction of the moon must always be taken into account, because even a slight error at the start of the journey could produce a considerable deviation from the desired course at the end.

If the moon revolved around the earth in a circular orbit, with the earth at the center, the distance of the moon would always be the same. But the orbit traveled by the moon around the earth is a slightly oval curve, which is called an *ellipse,* with the earth located a little off center. Therefore, we cannot talk about the distance to the moon. We can only talk about the distance to the moon at some particular point in its orbit. For example, during the month of January 1960 the moon was nearest the earth on the 26th, when its distance was 224,600 miles. It was farthest away on February 7, when its distance was 251,500 miles. But the moon's orbit is always changing. Thus by February 23 its orbit had changed so that it came within 228,100 miles at closest approach. It happened that the moon was near the new-moon phase at these close approaches, which might be a good time for launching a rocket to obtain a photograph of the back side of the moon when it is fully illuminated. As every astronomer knows, however, the moon's features are hard to make out near full moon under the flat lighting by the sun. Perhaps a better view could be obtained by waiting until the moon was near the quarter phase, when the shadows of the mountains and craters stand out more clearly. This was evidently the trouble with the photograph of the back side of the moon obtained by the Russians. The back side was near the full phase so that the surface features were not thrown into strong relief by shadows. As a result, the whole surface appeared of nearly uniform, flat illumination.

But you may object that the moon might not be so close to the earth when it is near the quarter phase. Just how much difference would this make?

Not nearly as much as you might think. Suppose we sent a missile into space from an altitude of 500 miles above the earth's surface, with the goal of reaching the moon on January 26, 1960, when the distance is 224,600 miles. We would require a starting velocity of 6.47 miles per second to go this distance and no farther. The trip would take about 117 hours.

Now suppose we tried to contact the moon when farthest from the earth, as on February 7, 1960, when its distance has increased to 251,500 miles. To reach this distance, starting again from 500 miles up, we would need an initial velocity of 6.48 miles per second. That additional velocity of only 0.01 miles per second at the start would be enough to send the rocket 27,000 miles farther into space at the finish. The trip would take about 10 hours longer.

We have calculated the velocity that is just sufficient to take the rocket to the moon and no farther. But if we are going to maneuver around the moon we should have a little velocity left over upon arrival. Incidentally, here we are neglecting entirely the attraction of the moon. It is wrong to assume that we can aim just to reach the "neutral" point where the gravitational field of the moon equals that of the earth, and the rocket will fall the rest of the way. The problem is not that simple.

So now suppose we send our rocket moonward from 500 miles up with a velocity just a little more than that needed to attain the minimum distance of 226,000 miles. Here are the results:

58

Starting velocity at 500 miles (miles per second)	Velocity upon arrival (miles per second)	Time of journey (hours)
6.6	1.28	49.6
6.7	1.72	32.5
6.8	2.08	26.9
6.9	2.38	23.7

This table shows how critically the missile's velocity upon arrival and the time of transit depend upon the starting velocity. Just for fun we might quit being conservative and make a calculation for a rocket starting 500 miles up with the impossibly high velocity of 8 miles per second. In this case it would reach the moon with a velocity of 4.7 miles per second, moving so fast it would scarcely be deflected at all by the moon's feeble gravitational pull. And the trip would take only 12.5 hours.

▶ *Why does such a little difference in starting speed make such a big difference in the time of transit?*

The slowdown comes mostly in the last half of the trip. Let us compare the times taken by two missiles to attain the same distance from the moon, one starting at 6.77 miles per second and the other at 6.99 miles per second. We will assume that we are starting from a body orbiting at a height of 200 miles above the surface, and that the distance of the moon is 226,000 miles:

Distance from earth's center	Time elapsed 6.77 mi/sec	Time elapsed 6.99 mi/sec
4,163 miles	0.0 hours	0.0 hours
26,317	1.7	1.5
48,470	4.4	3.7
70,624	7.8	6.1
92,778	11.9	8.8
114,932	16.4	11.6
137,085	21.4	14.6
159,239	26.8	17.4
181,393	32.6	20.5
203,546	38.8	23.5
225,700	45.3	26.7

59

To attain the halfway mark the rocket starting at 6.77 miles per second would require 16.4 hours, while the rocket starting at 6.99 miles per second would arrive there 5 hours sooner. But the slower rocket would take 29 hours to cover the last half of the distance, while the faster rocket would make it in only 15 hours, almost twice as fast. Thus an increase in velocity of only 0.22 miles per second at the start makes a difference of nearly 19 hours in the total elapsed time.

In other words, on the way to the moon it is the last hundred thousand miles that are going to be most affected by initial speed.

4 ▶ ECLIPSES OF THE SUN
   AND MOON

▶ *What causes an eclipse of the sun?*

The cause of an eclipse of the sun is very simple. The moon gets in front of the sun and blocks off all or part of it from our view. It is only by a kind of lucky cosmic accident that we ever have a total eclipse of the sun: the fact that the apparent size of the moon in the sky may be just a little larger than the apparent size of the sun. The moon is a body only 1000 miles from center to surface. The sun is a vastly larger body, 400,000 miles from center to surface. That is, the sun is four hundred times the size of the moon. But the sun is also four hundred times as *far away* as the moon, and a small body can cover up a larger body if it is close enough to the eye. A penny held at arm's length is big enough to cover the disk of the sun. So, although the moon is much smaller than the sun it is close enough to the earth to mask completely the disk of the sun. If the moon revolved in an orbit that took it just a little farther from the earth than it does we would never have a total solar eclipse, because the moon's disk would not appear quite big enough to cover the sun's disk. Even now this may happen when the moon is a little farther from the earth than the average. At such times the moon is directly in front of the sun but its disk is not quite near enough to cover the disk of the sun. As a result, we see the bright rim of the sun shining out around the black disk of the moon like a halo. Such an eclipse is called an annular or ring-shaped eclipse. The light of the sun shining through depressions around the moon's edge looks like glowing jewels set around the outside of a ring.

61

Eclipses of the sun always occur when the sun and moon are in line with the earth at new moon, and new moon occurs every month. Why then do we not have an eclipse of the sun every month, when the moon is new?

Imagine the sun and the earth floating around in a big pond so that half the sun and half the earth are out of the water, as suggested in Figure 26. Notice that the moon does not revolve around the earth on the surface. Half of the moon's path lies above the surface of the pond and half below it.

At *A* the moon is new; that is, it is approximately in line with

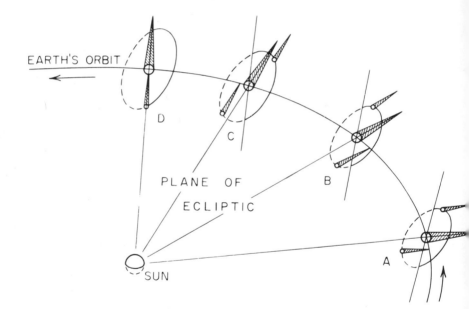

26. Since the moon's orbit is not in the plane of the earth's orbit, the shadow cone passes a little above or below the earth or moon at times, and no eclipse occurs.

the sun, but a little below the surface of the pond so that the moon's shadow misses the earth. At *B* and *C* the moon is new again, but still slightly below the surface; the tip of its shadow again misses the earth. Finally at *D* the moon is new and also lies on the surface of the water in which the earth and sun are floating. This time the tip of the moon's shadow touches the earth and we have an eclipse.

At other positions in the earth's orbit around the sun the moon passes by the earth a little above the surface on which the earth and sun are afloat. Only when the moon passes between the earth and sun very close to the surface can we have an eclipse. All this is due to the slight tilt of the moon's orbit in relation to the orbit of the earth around the sun.

In astronomical language, the surface of the pond is called the *plane of the ecliptic,* because it is in this plane or surface that *eclipses* occur. The place where the moon rises out of or above the ecliptic, or passes from below the water up into the air above it, is called the ascending node of the moon's orbit. The place at which the moon dips under the ecliptic is called the descending node. Eclipses can only occur when the moon is near one of its nodes. Only then can the shadow cone fall upon the surface of the earth and produce a solar eclipse.

▶ *What causes an eclipse of the moon?*

An eclipse of the moon occurs when the moon passes into the shadow of the earth. Here again, the moon must be near the surface in which you can think of the sun and earth as being partly submerged. Otherwise the moon will pass a little above or below the earth's shadow and so escape eclipse (see Fig. 26).

Although eclipses of the sun occur more often than those of the moon, we see many more eclipses of the moon than we do of the sun. The reason is that the tip of the moon's shadow, when it reaches the earth, is so small that it covers only a very small spot on the surface of the earth—never more than 167 miles in width. Therefore, only a very few people within the narrow path swept out by the shadow cone will see the sun in total eclipse. But an eclipse of the moon is visible to everyone on the right side of the earth. Also, an eclipse of the moon lasts much longer than an eclipse of the sun. The longest time a total eclipse of the sun can last is 7 minutes 40 seconds. An eclipse of the moon can last much longer. The thickness of the earth's shadow cone at the distance of the moon is 5700 miles. Since the moon travels at the rate of 2000 miles an hour it may remain partially within the shadow for more than two hours and may be total for 1 hour 40 minutes.

The smallest possible number of eclipses we can have in a year is two, both of the sun. The most that we can have is seven, five of the sun and two of the moon, or four of the sun and three of the moon. The most usual number of eclipses is four.

27. The lunar eclipse of January 29, 1953. Exposures taken at five-minute intervals as shadow of earth crept over surface of moon.

64

5 ▶ THE SUN AND ITS EFFECTS

▶ *What is the sun?*

The sun is a star, similar to many others in the sky. Only because the sun is so near the earth does it look so much brighter than other stars. The sun is the only star that shows a disk in our sky. All the other stars appear merely as points of light, even in the largest telescopes. No matter how much you magnify a star it still is a star. They are much too far away to show a disk as some of the planets do, even through a small telescope.

So the first answer to our question is that the sun is a star, the only star close enough to enable us to make detailed observations of its surface.

The sun is the ruler of the nine planets and thirty-one natural satellites of the solar system, controlling their motions by the force of its gravitational attraction. The sun is the only body outside the earth itself that is really necessary for our existence. People often suppose that the gravitational attraction of the stars and planets keep the universe in a delicate state of balance, so that the slightest upset of the forces involved would lead to disaster. As a matter of fact, all the bodies in the universe could be destroyed except the sun, earth, and possibly the moon, and few people would ever be aware of the fact. The stars are much too distant to exert any noticeable influence on the earth. And the planets disturb the motion of the earth to such a slight extent that only a few astronomers who specialize in such observations would notice the difference. The force of gravitation between the sun and earth is great enough to snap a steel cable 3000 miles thick. Yet this tremendous force causes the earth to depart from a straight line by only an inch while traveling 160 miles along its orbit.

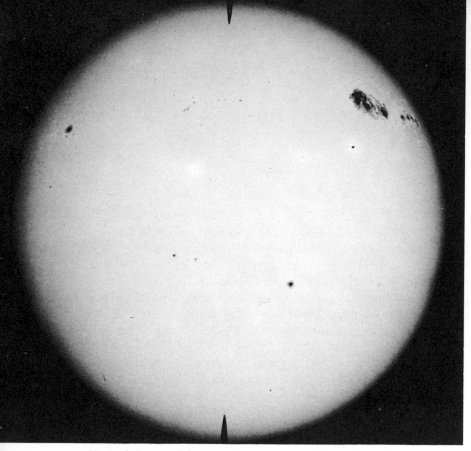

28. A whole view of the sun as it appeared on February 9, 1945. The large spot group was visible to the naked eye.

▶ How does the sun send us energy?

The sun is a gigantic light and power plant. Radiation from the sun is the source of all energy upon the earth. The heat produced from burning various substances is simply energy that was stored up from the sun, sometimes many millions of years ago in the form of oil or coal. Water power used to generate the electricity that illuminates a city had its origin in the sun: The warmth of the sun caused water from the ocean to evaporate; the water rose and condensed into a cloud; this cloud is carried inland and

66

further condenses into rain which falls to earth, forming streams and rivers whose water is caught in a reservoir and used for generating electrical power. We do not realize the enormous amount of work done by the sun in transporting water from the oceans to the land. An inch of rainfall over an area of a square mile means that about 60,000 tons of water have fallen. If the seasonal rainfall is 30 inches, this means that in the course of a year some 2 million tons of water have fallen over each square mile of the region. And all this energy comes from the sun.

Expressed in another way, suppose at the distance of the earth from the sun (93 million miles) there was a shell of ice 426 feet thick. The sun would melt the shell in one year. Or if there were a shell of ice 2200 feet thick surrounding the sun's surface it would all melt during the course of an hour. All the energy upon earth comes from the sun. The only possible exception may be energy from the nucleus of the atom. And even this energy may have come from the sun if the earth and other planets were once part of the solar envelope several billion years ago, as some astronomers believe.

▶ *Just how hot is the sun?*

From merely a glance at the sun we can see that it is a bright ball of fire that must be intensely hot to shine with such brilliance. The glowing filament of an electric light would look black against the disk of the sun; so would the white-hot crater of an electric arc. Therefore we know the sun must be much hotter. We might find the temperature of the surface of the sun by holding hotter and hotter objects in front of it until we finally found one so hot that it matched the sun in brightness. The trouble is we would have a hard time getting anything to such a high temperature for more than a very short time. A better way is to measure the total intensity of radiant energy from the sun that falls on, say, a square inch of surface in a minute. Then we can calculate the total amount of energy falling on the surface of a shell enclosing the sun at the distance of the earth. Since we know the size of the sun, we can now find how much energy is radiated per minute by each square inch of the surface of the sun itself. Then, from the laws of radiation, it is possible to determine the temperature of the surface of the sun—about 11,000° F. This is far hotter than most temperatures with which we ordinarily come in contact. No wonder the filament of an electric light looks dark against the sun: its temperature is only around 3000° F. Only in nuclear reactions do we encounter temperatures which for a few seconds exceed that of the sun.

▶ *How do astronomers tell what is in the sun and stars?*

More than a century ago the suggestion that we could tell what chemical elements are in the sun and stars would have been dismissed as fantastic. Astronomers in those days were much

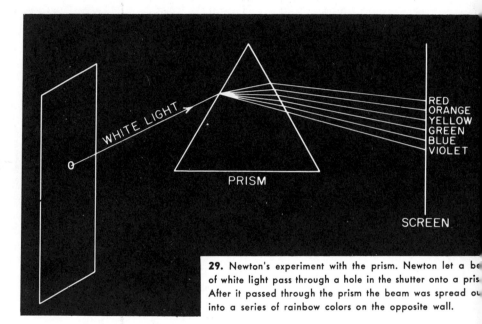

29. Newton's experiment with the prism. Newton let a be of white light pass through a hole in the shutter onto a pris After it passed through the prism the beam was spread ou into a series of rainbow colors on the opposite wall.

concerned about the exact position of the stars but had little interest in the nature of the stars themselves. Today the situation is wholly reversed. Comparatively few astronomers are concerned any longer with the fundamental problem of determining the positions and motions of the stars. A great many are absorbed in determining their chemical elements and the conditions under which these elements exist in the atmosphere of a star. The story of how this is done goes back to an experiment performed by Isaac Newton in 1666 in his rooms at Cambridge, England, when he was a twenty-three-year-old student there.

Newton's experiment was made with a prism; familiar to everyone of that time, it had not been used as a scientific instrument. Everyone knows that when white light shines through a triangular piece of glass or prism the light that comes out is no longer white but appears as a gradation of the different colors of the rainbow—violet, blue, green, yellow, orange, and red. This series of rainbow colors is called a *spectrum*. Newton studied the spectrum by admitting a beam of light into his darkened room through a hole in the shutter. This beam of light went through a prism and the different-colored rays were spread out on the opposite wall in a spectrum. Newton noticed that some rays were bent more than others, the violet rays being bent (refracted) the most and the red the least. The rainbow band of light apparently consisted simply of overlapping images of the hole in the shutter. Later Newton was able to produce a purer spectrum by letting the light come through a narrow slit instead of a round hole, thus reducing the overlapping. By putting a lens between the prism and the screen he was able to bring the colors to a sharp focus on the wall, in this way producing a true spectrum. This instrument in its crude form was the first spectroscope, the instrument for analyzing light into its separate colors. When, instead of merely being focused onto a screen, the rainbow strip is photographed by being allowed to fall on the sensitive surface of a photographic plate, the instrument is called a spectro*graph*.

Newton narrowly missed making another important discovery, probably because he used too wide a slit or because of the poor quality of his prism and lens. As it was, science had to wait a century and a half—until 1814—when a capital discovery was made about the solar spectrum by a German optician named Joseph Fraunhofer. He found that if the light of the sun passes through a sufficiently narrow slit the spectrum thus produced is crossed by dark lines which occur at different positions among the various colors. These dark lines are still called Fraunhofer lines. Fraunhofer made a map of the solar spectrum in which he charted the position of the different lines and designated them by letters

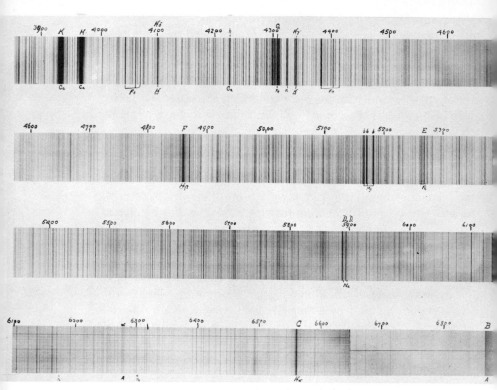

30. The solar spectrum, showing the dark Fraunhofer lines. These lines are produced by the chemical elements in the solar atmosphere.

which are still in use. Thus Fraunhofer's *C* line refers to a strong dark line in the red part of the spectrum. The *D* lines are two lines close together in the yellow. The *B* lines are in the green. Two very strong lines in the violet are Fraunhofer's *H* and *K*. Fraunhofer did not know the significance of these dark lines or how they were produced. That had to wait nearly another fifty years until more fundamental work was done in the laboratory. Later it was found that the dark Fraunhofer lines also occur in the spectra of the stars, although they are harder to observe since their light is so much weaker than that of the sun. Some stars were found that did not have as many dark lines as are found in the solar spectrum, while others have many more.

▶ *What do the dark Fraunhofer lines mean?*

The answer to this question was not found, as we have noted, until about fifty years after their discovery. Suppose that instead of examining the light of the sun we examine the light from some other source, such as the light from glowing iron or sodium vapor. These substances show a spectrum too, only it is not a long colored ribbon of light as the sun's is. Instead they show a spectrum consisting only of bright lines. But when these *bright* lines are compared with the *dark* lines in the solar spectrum they are found to match exactly. Thus two bright yellow lines in the spectrum of glowing sodium vapor fall at precisely the position of

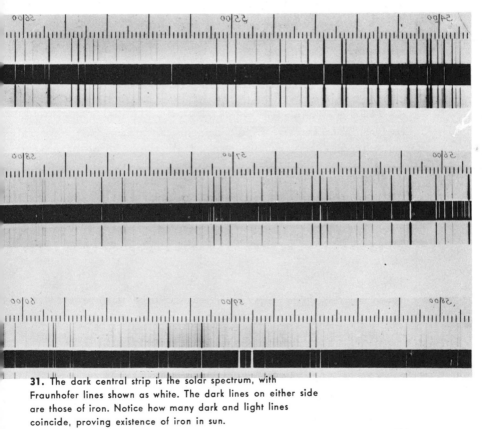

31. The dark central strip is the solar spectrum, with Fraunhofer lines shown as white. The dark lines on either side are those of iron. Notice how many dark and light lines coincide, proving existence of iron in sun.

71

Fraunhofer's two dark *D* lines in the sun. The glowing vapor of iron produces hundreds of bright lines, distributed all through the colors, each one matching a dark line in the solar spectrum. Such a coincidence can hardly be due to chance. It must mean that the elements sodium and iron are present in the atmosphere of the sun.

Here then is a comparatively easy way of finding what elements exist in the sun and stars. All we need to do is to match the dark lines in their spectra with the bright lines produced by different chemical elements in the laboratory. Some, such as iron, nickel, chromium, and manganese, produce many lines and identification is easy. Some substances (such as hydrogen) produce a series of lines from red into blue and violet. Some elements produce many lines but they do not match lines in the spectrum of the sun and stars. Since there are so many dark Fraunhofer lines in the solar spectrum we would expect some of them to match those of the elements by chance. If some of the weak lines of an element match Fraunhofer lines and the strong lines do not, then we know coincidence must be accidental. The identification of tin and gold in the sun depends upon the coincidence of only a few of the strongest lines in the spectra of these elements. At present, out of the 92 naturally occurring elements on the earth a total of 66 have been identified in the sun, most of them with certainty. It is probable that all 92 elements exist in the sun but some in such small quantities that they do not give observable lines. Also, in some cases the strongest lines of an element are in the far ultraviolet region of the spectrum; these cannot be observed by our earth-based instruments because they are absorbed by ozone in the upper atmosphere.

▶ *Why are the Fraunhofer lines dark?*

If we view a bright solid, such as the incandescent filament in an electric lamp, in a spectroscope we get simply a continuous ribbon of light made up of the colors of the rainbow. Suppose we let very bright light from a powerful electric lamp shine through the cooler flame of sodium vapor. If we examine the flame of sodium vapor by itself we see two bright lines—characteristic of this element—in the yellow. But when light from the electric lamp of *all* colors shines through the cooler sodium-vapor flame, we find there are two *dark* lines in the yellow where the *bright* lines would normally appear. If the current through the lamp is reduced so that the bright ribbon of spectrum grows weaker, the two dark lines will appear brighter, finally becoming indistinguishable from the spectrum of the lamp. Reducing the current through the lamp still further causes the yellow sodium lines to shine out as two bright lines on the faint spectral ribbon of the glowing filament.

We can use this experiment to interpret the solar spectrum. The main body of the sun, which is intensely hot, produces the continuous ribbon of rainbow light. The fact that it is crossed by dark lines must mean that the light from the intensely heated solar surface is shining through a cooler atmosphere of gases which surround the sun and absorb some of its light. This is the reason the lines appear dark. If the solar atmosphere were at a higher temperature than the surface of the sun they would appear bright. From a detailed study of the formation of the dark Fraunhofer lines astronomers can obtain a wealth of information concerning conditions in the solar atmosphere—for example, an estimate of the pressure, temperature, and electric and magnetic conditions that exist there.

▶ *What is the Doppler effect?*

It may seem incredible, but from a study of the dark lines in the spectrum of the sun or a star it is possible to tell whether the source of light is approaching or receding from the observer and how fast. This is known as the Doppler effect; it is difficult to explain in simple terms, since there is practically nothing like it that occurs in connection with our ordinary life.

It is not *quite* true that the two dark lines indicating sodium vapor in the spectrum of the sun occur at *exactly* the position of two bright lines of sodium vapor produced in the laboratory. If the sun and the laboratory on the earth are moving toward or away from each other the two lines will be slightly shifted in relation to one another. This shift is so small that it may appear too unimportant to be of any consequence. Yet it is extremely important to the astronomer. By measuring this shift he can tell not only whether the source of light (sun, star, or planet) is approaching or receding, but also how fast it is moving toward or away from the earth. If the object is approaching, the lines are shifted toward the violet. If the object is receding from us, the lines are shifted toward the red. The amount of the shift tells us how fast the body is approaching or receding.

The only analogy that explains *why* this is so occurs in connection with the whistle of a locomotive, an example that has been used so much it has become a classic in scientific literature. If a train is standing still, the pitch of the locomotive whistle remains the same. But if the whistle is blowing as the train approaches, its pitch sounds increasingly higher. Then, as the train rushes past, the pitch of the whistle drops abruptly. The reason is that when the train is approaching more vibrations from the whistle enter the ear per second than when the train is traveling away. The more vibrations, the higher the pitch; the fewer vibrations, the lower the pitch. In the case of light waves, an increasing number of vibrations per second causes a shift toward the violet—in the direction of higher frequency of vibrations of the light waves, corresponding to a higher pitch of the locomotive whistle. A decreasing number of vibrations per second causes a shift toward the red in the direction of lower frequency and corresponds to a lower pitch of the locomotive whistle.

This is the essence of the famous Doppler effect, certainly one of the most important principles known in physics. By measuring the shift in the spectrum lines of a star in comparison with those produced on earth we can tell how fast the star is approaching or receding. In the case of the sun, we can tell how fast various parts of it are moving in relation to the earth; we can measure the rate of rotation of the sun by this means. Or by examining the light from a planet we can measure its rate of rotation. The rotation periods of Uranus and Neptune were determined in this way. Any other means would have been unsuccessful, since these bodies show no spots on their surface.

▶ *What is a sunspot?*

A sunspot is a region on the sun that is cooler than its surroundings. The temperature in the center of a sunspot is about 8000° F. The temperature of the surface of the sun around

74

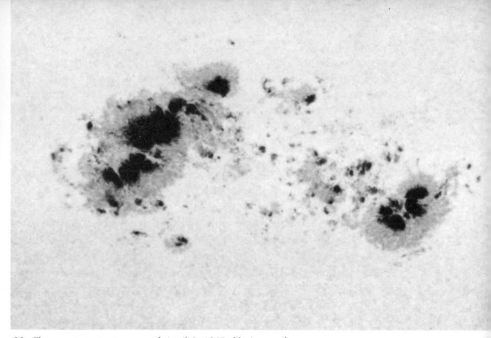

32. The great sunspot group of April 8, 1947. Notice cooler
dark central umbra, lighter surrounding penumbra, and
granulations over the solar surface.

the spot is about 11,000° F. The spot looks darker than the rest
of the sun simply because it *is* cooler and gives off less light than
the rest of the surface. If you covered the disk of the sun with a
sheet of cardboard, but left a small hole at the position of a spot,
you would find that the hole appears not dark but bright. In fact,
the filament of an electric light would appear dark viewed against
the background of a sunspot. Photographs are exposed so that the
surface of the sun looks about right on the printed picture. This
means that the spot is much underexposed and so looks black by
contrast.

You can see from Figure 32 that a sunspot is composed of two
parts. The dark central region is called the *umbra*. Surrounding
the umbra is a lighter area called the *penumbra*. The penumbra
looks as if it were composed of filaments extending from the bright
solar surface down to the umbra. Notice on the photograph that
the umbra does not fade out gradually into the penumbra, but
that there is a sharp dividing line between them. There is an
equally sharp division between the penumbra and the bright solar

surface. This in itself is rather surprising, for we might expect a sunspot to be darkest at the center and then brighten gradually until it merges with the surface around it. Why is there such a sharp division between umbra and penumbra, penumbra and solar surface? Nobody knows. If astronomers could answer this question they would doubtless have gone a long way toward finding what causes sunspots in the first place.

A refrigerator is a device that keeps its inside temperature lower than the surrounding temperature. A sunspot is a natural refrigerator on an enormous scale. Many sunspots last for weeks, or longer; the longest recorded duration of a spot group is 134 days, held by a group in 1919. Thus for more than four months there was a region on the sun larger than a cross section of the earth where the temperature was 3000° F. below that of its surroundings. In fact, to fix the idea you might think of sunspots as icebergs floating in the boiling solar sea.

What is the cause of the cooling in sunspots? Astronomers used to think it was gas rising from beneath the surface and cooling by expansion, but this idea has been abandoned. At present the cause of the cooling in sunspots is admittedly still unknown. It may be connected with the magnetic field found in every spot.

Sunspots have been compared to ferocious storms sweeping over the sun, like the cyclones that sweep over the surface of the earth. It is true that in some photographs the region around a spot appears to have a circular structure, as if it were whirling around, but more often this structure is poorly defined or missing altogether. No actual whirling motion has ever been measured around a sunspot. Instead of comparing spots to violent storms they would seem to be more like cool springs of water in a hot desert.

▶ *What is the solar cycle?*

If you kept count of the number of spots you can see on the sun each day for several months, you would find that they vary considerably from day to day. There would be some days when there were scarcely any spots visible, and others when there might be a dozen large groups consisting of perhaps dozens of individual spots. Throughout the year the spots would seem to break out and fade away pretty much at random, with no regu-

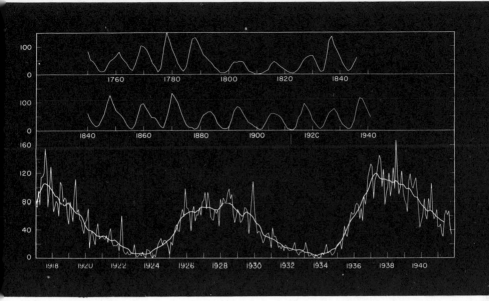

33. Smoothed sunspot curves for 1750 to 1940, with detailed
fluctuations in number of spot groups from 1918 to 1941.

larity in the way they come and go. Probably by the end of the
year you would be tired of counting them and ready to turn to
some sort of astronomical observation that is more immediately
rewarding.

To notice any systematic trend in the number of spot groups on
the sun you would have to keep count on them for at least ten
years, probably longer. Then you would notice from your counts
that there were years when the average number of spots on the
disk of the sun was definitely greater than others. And if you
kept watch on the sun long enough—for more than twenty years
—you would find that the number of spots increased and decreased in a period of about eleven years, as shown in Figure 33.
This eleven-year period in the rise and fall of sunspots is what is
known as the *solar cycle*. Notice that we said the length of the solar
cycle is *about* eleven years. The time from one low place in the
curve, or minimum, to the next minimum may be as short as 9
years or as long as 13.6 years. The average interval from 1755
to 1944 was 11.1 years.

▶ How was the eleven-year solar cycle discovered?

It takes a person with a very patient disposition to make a good sunspot observer. The man who discovered the solar cycle was probably one of the most patient individuals the world has ever known. On October 30, 1825, Heinrich Schwabe of Dessau, Germany, began observations of the sun with a 2-inch telescope in the hope of discovering a planet within the orbit of Mercury passing across the solar disk. But he soon became so absorbed in the ever-changing spots upon the sun that his original plan was forgotten. Schwabe kept a systematic record of all the spots he could observe on the sun on every clear day of the year. After twelve years of observation his records showed an indication of a rise and fall in sunspot activity with a period of about ten years. He published a summary of his results but did not feel justified in announcing the discovery of a ten-year cycle. Not until 1843, after having observed two maxima and two minima, did he feel justified in announcing the discovery of the solar cycle.

When he did announce it, the report attracted not the slightest attention. Schwabe's name was unknown in astronomy and apparently nobody bothered to read his modest little note in the *Astronomische Nachrichten.* Schwabe did not seem to have been bothered by this lack of recognition; he continued observing sunspots and working in his apothecary shop as usual. Not until eight years later when the famous philosopher Alexander Humboldt called attention to the discovery in his great work, *The Cosmos,* did recognition finally come. (Which shows the value of having a publicity agent even in astronomy!) And when Schwabe was presented the gold medal of the Royal Astronomical Society his work was hailed chiefly for demonstrating that there was still something to be discovered in the supposedly "exhausted" subject of astronomy!

But how many people would have carried on a project over so many years without any thought of reward or recognition? Suppose Schwabe had died before he had clear evidence of a rise and fall in sunspot activity? The prize could so easily have escaped him. Certainly few would have the time and patience to devote to such a prolonged investigation.

▶ What are solar granulations?

Suppose that you send the light of the sun through a telescope and, instead of looking at it directly, project the image onto a screen so that it can be seen by several people at once. At first glance you may think the solar image is the same brightness all over the disk. But if the air is very steady, so that the image is clear on the screen, you will notice that the surface of the sun is not uniformly bright but is covered by a kind of dusky veil that is especially prominent near the center of the disk. If the air is *very* steady you may be able to see that the surface of the sun is made up of small pores or *granulations,* some of which are so well marked that you can examine them individually. You will not be able to study one for long—probably less than a minute—before it begins to fade away and merge with other granulations around it. These granulations are the source of radiation on the surface of the sun or photosphere ("light" sphere).

You might think that astronomers would not be interested in the little solar granulations in comparison with markings on a much larger scale, such as the sunspots. Well, astronomers are interested in sunspots, but they are very much interested in the granulations, too. For the bright and dark spots formed by the granulations have long been believed to result from rising and descending currents of gas that transport energy from the hot lower levels of the sun's atmosphere to its surface. The difficulty has been in getting good photographs of the granulations. Seldom was the air still long enough to tell much about them with certainty. Various observations indicated the average granule was about 150 miles wide, moving up and down with a speed of something like 2 miles per second. But better observations were desirable, free from the disturbances that are present in the earth's atmosphere.

A step toward this goal was taken in the fall of 1957, when a 12-inch reflecting telescope was carried to an elevation of 80,000 feet by an unmanned skyhook balloon. Out of thousands of photographs obtained with an automatic device for tracking and photographing the sun, several were of the desired degree of sharpness and clarity. The granulations appeared quite different from the way they had looked in photographs taken from the surface of the earth. Instead of consisting of about an equal number of bright

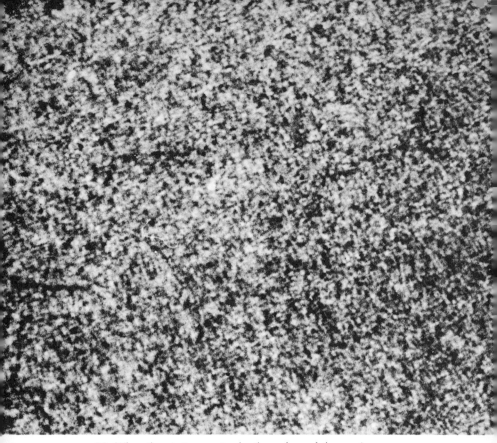

34. When the air is *very* steady, the surface of the sun is seen to be covered by a granular structure such as that shown here. Individual granules last only for a minute or two.

and dark spots, the granules were found to consist of bright cells separated from one another by dark, often very sharp lines. Thus instead of hot rising currents and cool descending ones of about the same size, there appear to be only thin lines of descending gas separating the rising columns.

▶ *What are solar flares?*

The simplest way to photograph the sun is to take a snapshot of it as you would of any other object, except that we usually have to dim down the light of the sun first, since it is so

80

bright that otherwise the picture of the sun would be completely "burned out." This solar photograph looks about the same as when the image of the sun is projected upon a screen, or seen through dark glasses. Such a picture is made up of all the light the sun sends us that is recorded upon the photographic emulsion.

But it is also possible with special instruments to photograph or view the sun in the light of a *single ray* emitted by one element only. For example, the hydrogen gas in the sun's atmosphere emits a strong red ray which scientists call H Alpha. It is now possible to isolate this red ray from the other colors in the sun's disk so that we view the sun in this light alone. When we do so the sun looks quite different from its appearance on a snapshot in light of practically all colors. The surface of the sun has a mottled look something like the waves of a storm-tossed sea, as shown in Figure 35. Near spots there are bright clouds of hydrogen gas, and the waves are generally drawn out into streaks that remind us of the lines of force formed by iron filings around the poles of a magnet. There are also dark streaks of gas overlaying the disk like long twisted ribbons.

When the sun is viewed or photographed in the red ray of hydrogen, sometimes over a sunspot group a small region will suddenly begin to glow more brightly than the rest of the solar disk around it. The bright region spreads rapidly and glows more intensely until it may cover an area considerably larger than the spot group itself. This bright-glowing region is called a solar flare. A flare reaches maximum brightness very quickly—usually in from 5 to 20 minutes—then fades away much more slowly, taking as long as an hour in the case of some very large flares. The cause of these flares is entirely unknown. Flares are classified on a scale of 1 to 3, depending upon size and brightness. Class 1 flares are fairly common, class 2 flares less so, and only a very few of great brilliance are classified as 3 or 3+. There are a handful of cases on record of a flare becoming so bright that it was visible without special equipment in white light directly on the disk of the sun. Thus on September 1, 1859, an English astronomer named Carrington, viewing the sun, was startled by some bright points of light that suddenly broke out around a large spot group, glowing like a star compared with the rest of the disk. Carrington was hardly able to believe his eyes, and became so excited he dashed out of his

81

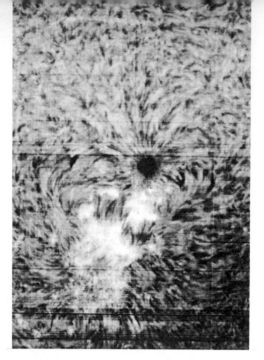

35. The surface of the sun as it appears when photographed in the light of only the red rays of hydrogen.

36. Vortexlike structure around an active spot group as photographed in red light of hydrogen.

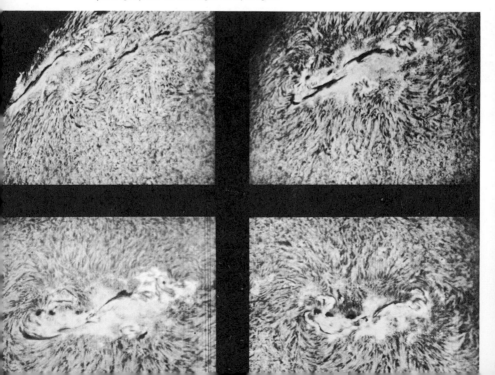

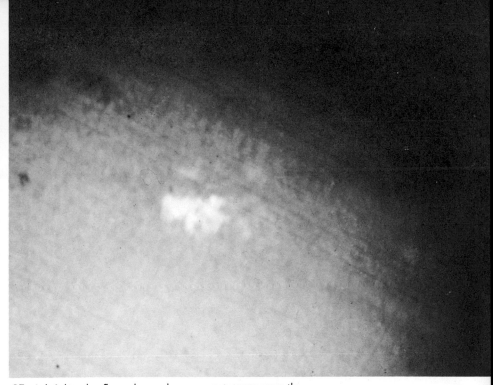

37. A bright solar flare observed over a spot group near the edge of the sun. Unlike other features on the solar disk, flares last for only a few minutes.

observatory in search of someone to verify the effect, evidently thinking that no one would believe him unless he could produce a witness. He found no one and when he returned to the sun the bright spots were much weaker. As it happened, an astronomer at another observatory in the British Isles was observing the sun at the same time, so there was no question of the reality of the effect.

This flare of 1859, one of the brightest on record, was followed by a violent magnetic storm. This has been found to be characteristic of the brightest flares (classified 3+). It has been found that sudden fadeouts in high-frequency radio signals often occur simultaneously with bright flares. This happens to be one case where we feel sure we know what is happening: Besides the *visible* light emitted by the flare, it also emits a great deal of invisible ultraviolet light. This ultraviolet light produces a sudden increase in the

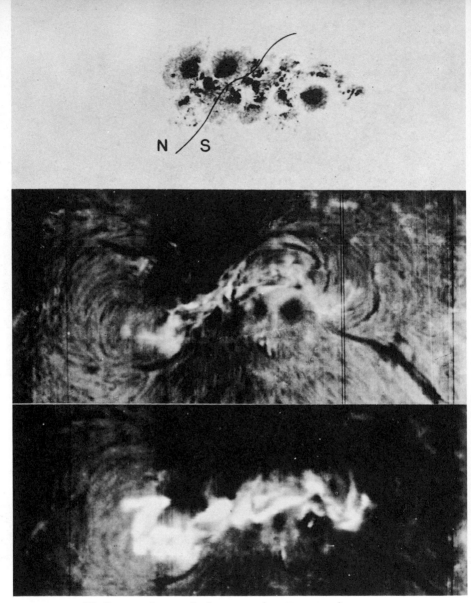

38. The top photograph shows normal appearance of sunspot group. The other two photographs show development of flare in hydrogen light.

number of charged particles in the high upper atmosphere. The radio waves, instead of being reflected back to earth in the upper atmosphere as usual, have their energy frittered away in giving random motion to these charged particles. After the flare dies out and the ultraviolet light from it no longer reaches the earth, the electrified particles recombine into neutral particles, so that the radio signals are now reflected back to earth as usual.

▶ What are solar prominences?

It is easy to tell *what* prominences are; that is, fairly easy to describe them. After that the going becomes tough. We don't know why there are prominences in the solar atmosphere, or why they behave as they do.

Viewed from above on the hydrogen photographs, solar prominences appear as long dark twisted ribbons winding over the sun's surface. Standing up at the edge of the sun, they look like flames projecting from the solar surface or clouds floating in the solar atmosphere. They bear some resemblance to the thin sheet of flame issuing from a fishtail burner in the laboratory. Prominences come in all shapes and sizes, so that it is as hard to talk about an "average" prominence as it is to talk about an "average" woman's hat. Many prominences, however, are 6000 miles thick, 125,000 miles long, and 30,000 miles high. Thus they are enormous

39. Prominences standing like sheets of flame at the edge of the sun.

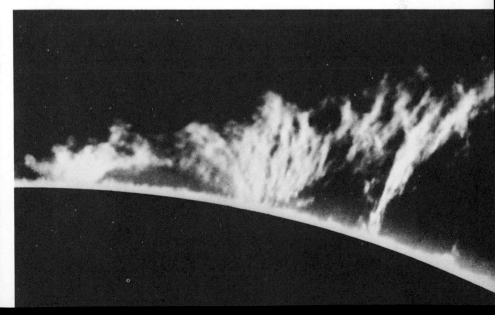

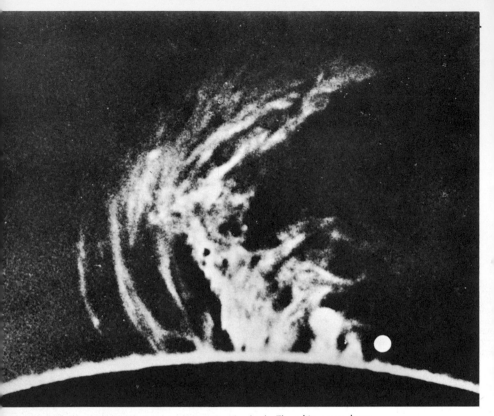

40. A prominence 140,000 miles high. The white spot shows the size of the earth. The streamers are probably moving into a center of attraction.

compared with the earth, but they are insubstantial, ghostlike things of very slight mass. Small prominences come and go in a few days, but 15 per cent survive for five, six, and seven solar rotations—about 150 to 200 days. Prominences would thus seem to have a slightly longer lifetime than sunspots.

The most spectacular views of prominences are those obtained by motion-picture photography. These pictures are taken by the time-lapse method, in which there may be an interval of a minute or more between exposures, so that the events of several hours can be shown on the screen in a very few minutes. At an eclipse the prominences are viewed for perhaps five minutes, during which they do not appear to change. Viewed by time-lapse photography, however, they are always changing—writhing and twisting about almost as if they were alive. One might expect prominences to be rising like vapor from the earth, but actually there is just about as much prominence material going down as there is coming up. One often sees prominences materializing, apparently out of nothing, like rain pouring out of a clear sky. Also, there seem to be centers of attraction in the solar surface which pull prominences into them, first sucking in a few streamers, then drawing over more material until the whole prominence finally rises up, arches over, and descends beneath the solar surface. Or perhaps the prominence is torn apart and vanishes in motion. These centers of attraction cannot be identified with spots or any other marking on the sun.

Prominences often start moving upward rapidly, going into sudden eruption as mysteriously as they are drawn beneath the surface. Many prominences are known to rise 100,000 miles above the surface, well into the region of the corona; one is known to have

41. Photograph showing the solar corona or pearly white envelope of light that flashes out around the sun when totally eclipsed.

extended a million miles from the edge of the sun. The fastest-moving prominence on record attained a velocity of 450 miles per second (1,600,000 miles per hour).

We are hardly able to speculate on the motions of prominences —they are so varied and complex. As one well-known astronomer expressed it, they move under a "combination of electrical, magnetic, and gravitational forces," which would seem to include about every kind of force likely to be operative on the surface of the sun.

▶ What is the sun's corona?

The *corona* is the pearly-white envelope of light that can be seen flashing out around the sun during a solar eclipse at the instant the sun is totally covered by the disk of the moon. Of course, the corona is always there, but since its light is only about one-millionth as bright as sunlight (half the brightness of the full moon), it is ordinarily blotted out by the sun's glare. During an eclipse the corona shines with an overpowering splendor; early astronomers felt it might be visible with a little help without an eclipse, and went around trying to glimpse the corona by getting the sun behind a distant mountain peak or a captive balloon. Such efforts always failed. In 1930, a Belgian astronomer, Bernard Lyot, finally succeeded in photographing the corona without an eclipse. Some people have a genius for painting pictures or playing the violin. Bernard Lyot had a genius for eliminating stray light from his instruments. His success may be partly attributed to the exceptionally clear sky above his 9400-foot-high observatory in the Pyrenees, but mostly it was a result of reducing scattered light in the lens system of his telescope to an absolute minimum.

The shape of the corona changes with the eleven-year solar cycle. At maximum of sunspot activity the corona forms a nearly circular envelope around the sun. Near sunspot minimum the corona extends out farther at the solar equator and is contracted into short tufts at the poles.

▶ What is coronium?

The solar corona emits certain rays of light which are not given off by the disk of the sun, the strongest being a ray in the green and another in the red portion of the spectrum. For years astronomers tried in vain to identify these rays with those given off by other chemical elements in the sun, but without success. About 1911 scientists suggested that the coronal rays are due to a hypothetical element called *coronium,* but since chemists had no place for such a new chemical element, the idea was never taken very seriously. Every effort to identify the mysterious substance that emitted the coronal rays ended in failure. Not until 1939 were the coronal rays finally identified, by a young Belgian astronomer named Bengt Edlén. He showed that under the extraordinary conditions that prevail in the corona certain rays that are "forbidden" under ordinary circumstances can be emitted in the rarified gas. These rays are not emitted by any strange substance, but by such common elements as iron, nickel, and calcium—but they only become visible when we look through a great depth of a very thin gas at a temperature of two million degrees Fahrenheit!

Some astronomers at first refused to believe that the gases in the corona could be at such a high temperature, but Edlén's identifications were so convincing that they have now been generally accepted. Even if we could produce a temperature of 2,000,000° F. in the laboratory we still could not get atoms of iron, nickel, and calcium to show the rays that we observe in the corona. The atoms there rarely produce one of these rays, so that we have to look through a great thickness of gas to see the coronal rays. In the laboratory we can only look through a few feet of pipe containing a gas. We have to look through a million miles of gas (as we do around the sun) to see the rays of the corona.

▶ *How does the sun affect the earth?*

Does the sun affect the earth in other ways than the obvious one of supplying it with light and heat? In looking for an answer, the spots that come and go on the solar surface would seem to be promising objects for investigation, since their number changes widely not only from month to month but also over the solar cycle of eleven years. Sunspots *look* so promising, in fact, that people have often kept track of them, not because they were interested in the spots themselves, but because they thought sunspots might have some connection with events on the earth. Thus, 150 years ago, Sir William Herschel made an investigation of a possible relationship between the weather and his sunspot counts. Since the weather records were poor in his day, Sir William used the price of wheat instead, but was unable to arrive at any certain conclusion about it. Since Herschel's time people have repeatedly tried to find relations between all sorts of changing quantities on the earth and sunspots, ranging from rainfall, business activity, epidemics, and wars to the fecundity of fur-bearing animals in Canada. Invariably all these investigations seem to end the same way—they never have enough data! Always the records are not quite long enough to give them a definite answer. Sometimes modern science comes along and ruins things. Thus one investigator turned up a splendid relationship between sunspots and diphtheria —until the discovery of diphtheria antitoxin put an end to that.

Of the scores of relationships that have been announced or suspected, only a few have withstood the test of time.

Sunspots do have some effect on the earth's magnetic field. The earth behaves as if it had a huge bar magnet inside it, with the north pole near Hudson Bay, and the south pole in the Antarctic continent. You can think of the strength of this magnet as represented by lines of magnetic force, extending from one pole to the other, such that the strength of the magnetic force is greatest where the lines of force are thickest. The lines of force are also directed in space as they extend from pole to pole. These lines of force constitute the earth's magnetic field. Both the strength and direction of the earth's magnetic field change with the sunspot cycle. That is, during the maximum of sunspot activity disturbances in the earth's magnetic field are more numerous than they are around sunspot minimum. The relationship only holds when averages are taken over a long time, such as a year. When averages are taken for shorter intervals, such as a month or less, the relationship seems to vanish into thin space. Also, magnetic activity seems to lag a little behind sunspot activity. That is, the peak in magnetic activity usually comes about a year after the peak in sunspot activity.

The changes in the magnetic field just mentioned are of a fairly regular type and occur in varying degree every day. Occasionally, however, the earth's magnetic field will be abruptly and violently disturbed by what is called a *magnetic storm,* which begins at practically the same time all over the earth. Magnetic storms, un-

90

like the smaller changes in the earth's field, occur when large groups of spots are on the sun more often than would be expected by chance. The most likely time for a magnetic storm to start is when a large spot group is near the center of the solar disk or slightly past it. But there are numerous exceptions. Occasionally the rotation of the sun on its axis will cause a large spot group to pass across the face of the sun and hardly cause a ripple on the magnetic record.

Displays of the northern lights (aurora borealis) are also most numerous and spectacular around sunspot maximum and especially so during a magnetic storm. These displays of the northern lights are brightest near (but not at) the north magnetic pole, and on rare occasions are seen in the southern part of the United States. Similar auroral displays also occur near the south pole; here they are called the aurora australis.

Just how spots on the sun, 93 million miles away, can produce these effects on the earth is still not really known. It is believed they may be caused by electrically charged particles, ejected from the sun at high speed, which reach the earth after a journey of several days. Large spot groups may eject electrified particles in bursts to cause the magnetic storms. The eleven-year rise and fall in magnetic activity may be the result of weaker emission from spot groups in general. Occasionally the outburst from a large spot group may fail to happen, or if it does happen the electrified cloud may miss the earth, so that no magnetic storm results. The whole subject is still in a very confused state although it has had intensive study by astronomers for more than a century.

▶ *Can we tell what lies below the surface of the sun?*

We can see only the outside top surface of the sun, the surface that contains the granulations and the sunspots. We have no way of telling from direct observation about conditions beneath the visible surface. But from our knowledge of the behavior of matter at high temperatures and pressures we can make an estimate of conditions all the way to the center of the sun. We know the total mass of the sun. It is equal to 330,000 times the mass of the earth. We know the size of the sun. It is 432,000 miles from center to surface. Knowing its total size and mass we can find its density, or the average amount of matter in a certain volume of space—for example, the average amount of matter per cubic inch. In this way we find that on the average the sun is about 40 per cent heavier than water.

Knowing the size, mass, and average density of the sun, we can proceed by mathematics to construct, layer by layer, a model sun which we believe will be like the real sun that we see in the sky. There is one fact about the sun which is a big help in guiding us in our solar construction work. Except for the spots on its surface, the sun never changes. It shows no tendency to explode or collapse. This means that the sun is a stable body. So the model sun we construct must also be stable. If we find the model sun we are building is so hot at the center that it would explode, or so cold that it would collapse, we know that we are on the wrong track and must start over again. It would take too long to recount all the details of such calculations, or the various model suns that have been constructed since about 1926. Here we will give the results for one of the most recent models of the sun as we believe it exists today.

The sun consists mostly of the two lightest gases, hydrogen and helium—about 75 per cent hydrogen and 25 per cent helium. The heavy elements, such as iron, nickel, cobalt, and the like, are present in such small quantities as to seem mere impurities mixed with the hydrogen and helium. At the surface of the sun the gases are much more rarified than the air we breath. As we bore inside the sun the amount of matter we encounter increases very slowly; in fact, we have to go about halfway to the center before the density of the material equals that of water. But after that the density increases rapidly. At two thirds of the way to the center the density is the same as that of copper. About three quarters of the way the density reaches that of gold. After that, the density rises above that of any substance known upon the earth. At the center of the sun the density of the material is believed to be 90 times that of water, or some 12 times the density of iron. Thus most of the material of the sun is in a dense central core which begins about halfway to the center. In fact, almost all of the sun is within 259,000 miles (60 per cent) of the distance from its center. You might reasonably think of the sun as being like a ball with a lead core which fills about half of it, the rest being made of cork. The temperature also increases toward the center, although not so sharply as the density. This table shows how the temperature of the sun rises as you go inward:

Distance below surface	Temperature
0.00	11,000° F.
.10	750,000
.20	1,500,000
.40	3,750,000
.60	8,000,000
.80	16,500,000
.90	22,000,000
1.00	25,000,000

Despite the fact that matter is packed more tightly at the sun's center than any substance known on earth, the sun is gaseous throughout. How can it be gaseous when it is denser than any metal? Because the temperature is so high. Also, the atoms are much smaller than they are in the outer atmosphere of the sun, where the gas is cold compared to its temperature deep inside. The size of the atom is determined by the electrons that circulate around outside the central nucleus like a cloud. If the temperature is very high, many of these electrons will be torn from the atom, leaving only the tiny bare nucleus. Hence, although the particles of matter near the center of the sun are packed very tightly together, they are so small there is still plenty of room left for them to circulate about as a gas. Think of a barnyard so filled with elephants that the animals can hardly move. The elephants correspond to the atoms in a liquid or solid. Replace the elephants with an equal number of guinea pigs. Now there would be plenty of room for them to run around in. This corresponds to the stripped atoms in a highly heated gas.

▶ *What makes the sun shine?*

For millions of years men simply took the sun for granted. The sun looks the same every day. It shows no sign of getting hotter or colder. Of course the weather changes during the year with the seasons, but that has nothing to do with the quantity of heat emitted by the sun. The light of some stars changes considerably in the course of a few days—or even minutes—but the light of the sun is remarkably steady. The most careful measurements have failed to reveal any definite evidence that its light ever really changes. In fact, we have direct evidence that the light of the sun cannot have changed perceptibly during the last three thousand years, since grapes and olives, plants extremely sensitive to temperature changes, have been cultivated regularly in the same regions that grew them in the days of Homer.

Doubtless, men have always propounded theories of some sort to account for the source of the sun's heat, but the first *rational* theories were not advanced until about 1850, soon after discovery of the fact that energy can neither be created nor destroyed, but only changed from one form to another. Consider a rifle bullet flying through the air. It has a certain amount of energy from its motion. The bullet strikes a target. What happens to the energy? It is not lost, but goes largely into heating the bullet and the target against which it strikes. Earlier ideas about the source of what keeps the sun shining had been little more than fanciful speculation. For example, Sir William Herschel's notion that the bright surface of the sun is a result of the decomposition of the solar atmosphere into clouds, with the emission of light and heat; or the idea of his son that the vital energies of monstrous creatures were the source of luminosity. There were two famous theories of the source of the sun's heat that originated about 1850. Although discarded now, they still are accorded respectful mention because they contain at least some basis in sound physical reasoning.

The theory of the meteoritic origin of the sun's heat was announced in 1848 by Robert Mayer. He pointed out that space is known to be filled with innumerable small bodies—meteorites—which must be drawn into the sun with a speed as high as 380 miles per second. As these meteorites plunge into the sun their energy of motion is changed into heat. Mayer calculated that a total mass equal to only 1/74th of the earth's, striking the sun every year, would be enough to make up its observed energy output. At first glance this seems quite reasonable and for a few years Mayer's theory enjoyed considerable success. Then somebody pointed out that if this were true then the earth should be receiving millions of times more heat from meteoritic bombardment than is known to be

94

the case, so that the theory soon became of historical interest only.

A theory ascribing the source of the sun's heat to friction, but in a way wholly different from the meteoritic hypothesis, was first described by the great German physicist Helmholtz in a popular lecture he delivered in 1854. He pointed out that as the sun loses heat by radiation it must contract, and this contraction amounts to the fall of particles toward the center of the sun by different amounts. Making the case as unfavorable as possible, Helmholtz found that a shrinkage of only 250 feet per year, an amount too small to be detected for ten thousand years, would be enough to supply the sun's yearly output of energy.

The contraction theory sounded so reasonable that astronomers soon became convinced of its truth, so much so that they arbitrarily told the geologists that the age of the earth could not be more than 25 million years and that they must adjust their evolutionary scale accordingly. This the geologists flatly refused to do, since they had good reasons for believing the age of the earth was at least 100 million years.

Toward the close of the nineteenth century, the discovery of radioactivity and the isolation of radium led to the uneasy suspicion that friction might not be the sole source of solar radiation. T. C. Chamberlain, a geologist, dared to challenge the contraction theory and to predict boldly, with startling insight, sources of subatomic energy. "What the internal constitution of the atoms be is yet open to question," he wrote in 1899. "It is not improbable that they are complex organizations, and the seats of enormous energies. . . . Are we quite sure we have yet probed the bottom of the sources of energy and are able to measure even roughly its total sum?"

After the reluctant abandonment of the contraction theory there followed a long period during which astronomers could give no definite answer to the question "What is the source from which the sun draws its power?" They could watch radium release enough energy every hour to melt more than its own weight of ice, knowing it could continue to do so for another thousand years. Application to the sun, however, seemed little more than a hopeful possibility. No radioactive substance had been identified in the sun and there seemed little prospect of finding one there. Besides, nobody had the faintest notion whence radium got its energy. Then, in

1905, Einstein published a paper of less than five hundred words which changed the whole situation and has continued to exert an ever-increasing influence on modern physics. He showed that if a body gives off energy, L, in the form of radiation, its mass is diminished by L/V^2, where V is the velocity of light.* From this

*This is the way Einstein originally wrote it.

he concluded "it is not impossible that with bodies whose energy content is variable to a high degree (for example, with radium salts) the theory may be put to a successful test."

There appeared to be two ways by which mass might be changed into energy. The more radical involved the total destruction of matter, as in the case of a head-on collision of an electron and a proton, in which both vanish, only to reappear as radiant energy. There could be no doubt that such a process within the deep interior of stars would certainly provide a potent source of energy. The chief drawback was the total absence of observational evidence to support it. A less energetic but more likely reaction was the formation of heavier elements from hydrogen. For example, in the formation of helium from hydrogen a little mass appeared to be lost, presumably released in the form of radiation. But attempts to formulate a theory of stellar evolution based upon changing hydrogen to helium were always strained. Every argument led to a deadlock. "Unfortunately, the facts as yet do not fall into satisfactory order," the famous astrophysicist Sir Arthur Stanley Eddington wrote in 1926, "and we are still groping for a clue."

By 1939, however, both our experimental and theoretical knowledge of nuclear reactions had progressed to such an extent that it was possible to decide which ones might be responsible for the production of energy in stars like the sun. First, all nuclear reactions that might conceivably contribute to generating energy in the sun were written down. Then, opposite each reaction was written the quantity of energy liberated, the rate at which the reaction would proceed at the estimated temperature for the center of the sun, and finally the average time required for the reaction to take place.

Inspection of such a table reveals that only a very few reactions provide energy at the rate emitted by the sun. Some reactions would occur so rapidly that the sun would explode, while others are far too sluggish. In fact, only two reactions appear to be capable of satisfying all the conditions. In one reaction two hydrogen atoms collide to form heavy hydrogen or deuterium, from which by further collisions with hydrogen the element helium is formed. This is the so-called proton–proton reaction. The other, called the carbon cycle, consists of a chain of reactions beginning with a collision between carbon and hydrogen, yielding nitrogen, whence by further collisions with hydrogen the elements nitrogen and oxygen are formed, in the end reverting to the original carbon with the formation of a new helium atom. At first it was thought that the energy of the sun was derived largely from the carbon cycle, but as the processes were studied more critically scientists have come to believe that the proton–proton reaction supplies more of the solar energy, while the carbon cycle is more effective in stars hotter than the sun.

▶ *How does sunshine affect us?*

We are so accustomed to sunshine in abundance that we are apt to take it as a matter of course. It is a commonplace. But actually sunlight is mysterious stuff, highly complex, made up of a long series of rays in widely different proportions. These rays react upon us in different ways, depending upon our age, sex, complexion, and general physical condition. Most of these rays are necessary and beneficial to plant and animal life. A very small portion have remarkable curative powers if properly used. There are a few that would be deadly if they could reach us. Suppose we go to the sun and examine the light emitted there. Then let us select a beam and follow it down to the surface of the earth.

From the surface of the sun at 11,000° F. there pours forth an apparently endless, steady stream of radiation. So far as we can tell from geological records, there is no reason to believe the sun is any cooler now than in the days of the dinosaurs.

According to current ideas, this vast Niagara of light comes from the body of the sun itself, by the conversion of its mass into radiant energy. If so, the sun is losing mass at the rate of nearly five million tons per second; quite a sizable amount, but still not enough to cause us alarm for many millions of years.

The visible light is only a small part of all the radiation the sun sends us. White light is, of course, really a mixture of rainbow colors running from violet at one end of the spectrum through

97

blue, green, yellow, orange, and red at the other. Beyond the red and violet is a long series of rays we cannot see but which nevertheless is of the utmost importance. At the red end, the spectrum reaches out to ten times its visible length into the infrared region. On the opposite side it extends into the ultraviolet about half as far again as the visible light. These ultraviolet rays, while they constitute only a small fraction of the whole, are by far the most interesting—and potent—of all the light the sun sends us.

Suppose sunlight were a marketable commodity, sold on the basis of the amount of energy contained in the different wavelengths. This is not a far-fetched comparison, for indirectly the sun is the ultimate source of all wealth. Green plants supply the world with food, and coal and oil are only another form of solar energy.

We will take yellow light, therefore, as our standard and quote its energy at $1. The red would sell at about 75 cents and the price would drop slowly as we go into the infrared, until the deepest infrared rays the sun sends us could be bought at around 12 cents. Going in the opposite direction, the light becomes increasingly energetic and the price would go up accordingly. Ordinary visible violet light would be quoted at $1.50 and the "near" ultraviolet rays—the kind that cause sunburn—at $2. Although the sun is too feeble a radiator to emit many X rays or cosmic rays, it is interesting to consider their cost on the same scale. The price would range all the way from $50, for a "soft" X ray, up to $60,000 for the very penetrating gamma rays. A cosmic ray would bring at least $6,000,000.

The sun does not emit all these rays in equal proportions. A sample analysis of a beam would show it to be roughly 43 per cent visible light, 42 per cent infrared, and 15 per cent ultraviolet. These rays constitute a strange mixture. The visible and the infrared rays mean light and heat for the earth, to supply energy for plant growth and the power to operate dynamos. In the ultraviolet region there is a narrow band of radiation that reaches the earth which is specific in the cure of rickets. And there are still others that would blister the skin and cause blindness if we had to stand them unprotected for only a short time.

But before a beam of sunlight can reach us it must first pass through the 100 miles of atmosphere that surrounds the earth, and here is where we are saved. For from 25 to 40 miles overhead is a gas called ozone that stops the blinding ultraviolet light as effectively as a stone wall. Ozone might be called an oxide of oxygen, for it is oxygen in a slightly more complex and active form than the kind we breathe. The pungent odor after a lightning display is attributed to ozone. In minute amounts it is rather refreshing, but in larger quantities it acts as a poison and may even cause death. If this protecting layer of ozone were brought down to sea level, it would, owing to the greater pressure there, be just about one eighth of an inch thick—a flimsy, unstable mass of molecules. Any upset in the equilibrium that now prevails in the upper atmosphere would be disastrous for us all. We could protect ourselves by staying out of the sun and wearing dark glasses, but vegetation would be speedily destroyed by sunlight in the ozone region.

But ozone does not stop quite *all* the ultraviolet rays. Some of these that can cure rickets and cause sunburn differ only slightly from those that are entirely harmful. This is one of the remarkable discoveries of modern times: the fact that a limited number of the ultraviolet rays we receive can create a form of vitamin D in the skin, specific in the cure and prevention of rickets. This substance is similar in action to the vitamin D found so abundantly in fishes, particularly cod and halibut. How fishes acquire so much vitamin D is still imperfectly understood. It now appears probable that at least a portion is synthesized within the fish itself, rather than derived from something it eats. Thus the sunshine vitamin can be obtained either by direct exposure to the sun or bottled in the form of fish oil.

Because sunlight is of such marked benefit in the treatment of a few diseases, its general value in promoting health has been greatly overestimated. An abundance of sunshine is not vitally necessary for good health and too much can be definitely harmful, as it is in producing certain forms of skin cancer. The most familiar and obvious result of first exposure to the sun is, of course, a burn. It is caused entirely by a few invisible ultraviolet rays that barely escape absorption by the ozone. Eliminate them and you would never be tanned at all. This is what has happened to sunlight that has passed through ordinary window glass, which is a strong absorber in this region. The immediate reddening of the skin upon exposure is a temporary effect produced by the heat from the visible and infrared rays. These penetrate much farther into the skin than those in the ultraviolet, and therefore are of most value in the treatment of deep-seated pain, such as sprains and bruised muscles.

The most dangerous thing about sunburn is that we are unaware of it until several hours later. Individuals differ so widely in this respect that each person should carefully determine the amount of sunlight he can safely endure without being too much influenced by the experience of others. A blond may be anywhere from 40 to 170 per cent more sensitive than a brunet. As a rule, men are more sensitive than women, and people between the ages of 20 and 50 more sensitive than the average. The effect also depends upon the general health: people with a high-strung, nervous disposition or high blood pressure are apt to be unusually sensitive. Different parts of the body also differ greatly in sensitivity. The arms can stand 50 per cent more than the chest and back, and the legs a little more than the arms.

The skin can be protected by applying certain ointments that are fluorescent; that is, they will glow in the sunlight. They absorb the ultraviolet rays and then promptly emit them again, but usually in the form of visible light. Their action for the body roughly corresponds to that of ozone for the entire earth.

The chief objection to sunlight as a curative agent is that it is so undependable. Sometimes we get too much and at other times practically none at all, depending upon the seasons, the weather, and local conditions. Fortunately, the beneficial rays from the sun are also present in several artificial light sources, which can be regulated at will.

Mysterious powers are often attributed to the "vibrations" emanating from these lamps, which are supposed to have peculiar healing effects not found in sunlight. It is true that light from a mercury-vapor arc, for example, contains some of the rays that are stopped by ozone; and they are generally richer in violet light than is sunlight. Also, because the sun is 93 million miles away and the lamp only a few feet, more light is received from the lamp per unit area of surface. But there is no essential difference in the rays themselves. Violet light from an artificial source and violet light of the same color from the sun are both violet light—enthusiastic claims of the manufacturer notwithstanding.

We have become adapted to life near a star of moderate temperature that emits more visible light than any other kind. But stars exist with surface temperatures several times higher than ours, up to 50,000° F. in certain cases. With a star of this type for a sun, we would have to adjust ourselves to radiation of entirely different composition from sunlight. For although such a star would give out more rays of all kinds than the sun does, the great bulk of it would be far out of sight in the ultraviolet, invisible to eyes like ours.

At the other end of the scale are red stars with surface temperatures as low as 3000° F. They radiate most strongly in the infrared region, and give out almost no violet or ultraviolet light.

An interesting combination of the two extremes is found in the case of the remarkable variable star, Omicron Ceti, or Mira. It has an intensely hot white dwarf star for a companion, while Mira is a cool star. Here we have a strange mingling of high and low energy radiation in widely different amounts.

6 ▶ HOW THE PLANETS MOVE

▶ *How do the planets move around the sun?*

Suppose you could soar out into space many millions of miles until you were at a point somewhere above the north pole of the sun. Then, looking down on the solar system you would see the planets moving around the sun in paths as shown in Figures 43 and 44. They would appear to be revolving around the sun in the opposite direction from the motion of the hands of a watch. You would notice too that the planets nearest the sun move the fastest. In the figures the arrows indicate the relative velocities of the planets in their orbits. It can be seen that the velocities of the planets range from about 30 miles per second in the case of Mercury to only about 3 miles per second in the case of Neptune. The speed with which a planet moves in its orbit depends upon its distance from the sun. The smaller the distance the faster the motion. This is because the gravitational pull of the sun is greatest for the planets nearest to it. The inward pull of the sun changes the direction of motion of the planets just enough to keep them revolving in their present orbits.

The speed of a planet also changes as it moves in its orbit. The orbits of the planets look as if they are circles but actually they are another kind of curve, called an *ellipse*—elongated oval-shaped curves of the sort shown in Fig. 45. It is almost as easy to draw an ellipse as a circle. Set two thumbtacks on top of a drawing board and pass a string around them. Then take a pencil and move it around the tacks, keeping the string taut at all times. The type of ellipse you get will depend upon the separation of the tacks. If the tacks are set close together you will get an ellipse that is hard to distinguish from a circle. (Indeed, a circle is simply an

42. Views of Venus, Mars, Jupiter, and Saturn.

103

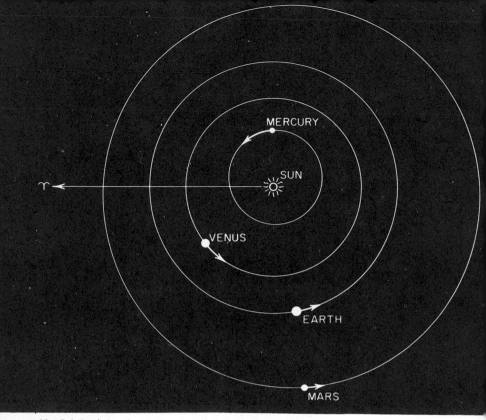

43. Orbits of the planets Mercury, Venus, earth, and Mars.
Arrow lengths indicate relative orbital velocities (positions for
January 1, 1961).

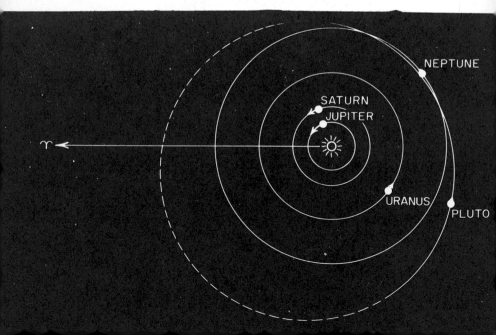

ellipse in which the two tacks coincide.) If the tacks are set far apart you will get a very elongated ellipse that resembles a cigar. The planets move in ellipses that are nearly circular. Comets usually move in greatly elongated ellipses. Let us look at a moderately elongated ellipse such as that shown in Fig. 45.

The tacks are at two points, called the *foci,* within the ellipse. In the orbit of a planet the sun is always at one focus of the ellipse. There is nothing but vacant space at the other. The point on the ellipse closest to the sun is called *perihelion.* The point farthest away is called *aphelion.* We have now introduced all the technical terms we shall need for the discussion of the motion of a planet around the sun in its elliptical orbit.

The planet moves fastest when it is nearest the sun at perihelion and slowest when it is farthest from the sun at aphelion. But this does not describe its motion very accurately. We want to know how the planet moves in *any* part of its orbit.

▶ *How were the laws of planetary motion discovered?*

Johannes Kepler (1571–1630), a German astronomer, mathematician, and writer, was the first person to discover the laws governing the motion of a planet in its orbit, probably about 1609. He arrived at his conclusions from a study of the motions of Mars entrusted to his care by Tycho Brahé (1546–1601), a Danish nobleman who devoted himself to the study of the stars and who became one of the greatest observational astronomers of all time. It was Kepler's job to find a type of orbit for Mars that would agree with Tycho's observations. In those days it was supposed that the sun, moon, and planets revolved around the earth in a combination of circular motions which represented tolerably well for a short time the paths followed by the planets against the background of stars. The trouble was that planetary tables constructed on this basis were never good for any length of time. Kepler had at his disposal the most accurate series of observations of Mars so far made. He tried one combination of circular motions after another but without success. (Here we omit the details of how these circular motions operated. It is hard enough to learn about how things work the *right* way, without wasting time studying how they work the *wrong* way.) At one time

105

4. Orbits of Jupiter, Saturn, Uranus, Neptune, and Pluto. rrows indicate relative orbital velocities. The greater their stance from the sun, the more slowly planets move.

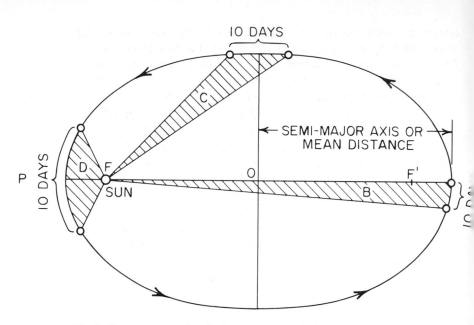

45. A planet moves so that the line joining it with the sun sweeps over equal areas in equal times. The shaded areas swept over in ten days are all equal.

he was able to describe Tycho's observations so closely that the greatest difference between the calculated and observed position of Mars could hardly be discerned by the eye. (All Tycho's observations were made before the invention of the telescope.) But Kepler had so much confidence in Tycho's work that he discarded his own calculations without hesitation and started in all over again.

As a result of trying one system of planetary motion after another, at the end of twenty years Kepler finally found three laws of planetary motion. They are so extraordinarily simple that it is hard to understand now how they could have so long escaped him. The first law says that the orbit of every planet is an ellipse with the sun at one of its foci. The second law says that the line joining the planet with the sun sweeps over equal areas in equal intervals of time. This property of planetary motion is illustrated in Fig. 45. Consider the motion of the planet when it is near perihelion, at P. The line joining the planet with the sun is short here, but the planet moves most rapidly in this part of its orbit, sweeping out the shaded area D in ten days. Now consider the motion of the planet when near aphelion, at A. The line joining the planet with the sun is much longer than at P and hence sweeps over more area, but the planet moves more slowly than at P. In the course of ten days it sweeps over the area B. The shaded areas D and B are equal. At some intermediate position the area C, swept over by the line joining the planet with the sun in ten days, is also equal to the areas B and D.

Kepler's third, or harmonic law, requires a little algebra. It says that the squares of the periods of revolution of the planets are proportional to the cubes of their mean distances from the sun. Let us express the periods of revolution of the planets in years, and their distances in terms of the distance of the earth from the sun. This distance of 93 million miles from the earth to the sun is our yardstick in the solar system and is called the astronomical unit. Let us see how the harmonic law works. Mars revolves around the sun in 1.88 years at a mean distance of 1.52 astronomical units. The square of the period is 1.88×1.88 or 3.53. The cube of the distance is $1.52 \times 1.52 \times 1.52$ or 3.51. Thus it is seen that the two are nearly equal, and if you care to try it, you will find that the same relation holds for the other planets, too.

Kepler speculated a good deal about the nature of his laws, without arriving at anything of value. That is, he was never able to "explain" them in terms of some more fundamental physical principle. He only knew that for some reason they worked. A complete solution was not forthcoming until 1687, when Isaac Newton published his great work, the *Principia,* which has been called possibly the most important scientific work ever written. In this book Newton fully discussed the laws governing the motions of bodies in general and of the planets in particular. He showed further that the three laws of Kepler are merely different aspects of the single law of gravitation and can be derived from it. This law states that every particle of matter in the universe attracts every other particle of matter in the universe with a force that is directly proportional to the product of their masses, and inversely proportional to the square of the distance between them.

And what is the physical basis for the law of gravitation? That is a question for which we are still seeking the answer.

107

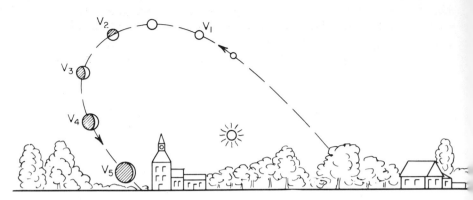

46. Venus as an evening star viewed after sunset in the western sky. Appearing from behind the sun as a nearly full disk at V_1, it comes around in front of the sun as thin crescent at V_5.

▶ What are the terrestrial planets?

As the name indicates, the terrestrial planets are the ones similar to the earth in size and composition. They include the moon, Mercury, Venus, Mars, and Pluto. We might also include the larger satellites of the solar system, such as the four large moons of Jupiter, Titan, the largest satellite of Saturn, and the satellite of Neptune, bodies which are about the size of Mercury. Except for the large satellites, the terrestrial planets have a fairly high density, between that of aluminum and iron.

▶ What are the giant planets?

The giant planets are Jupiter, Saturn, Uranus, and Neptune. They are much larger bodies than the terrestrial planets, both in size and mass. That is, they occupy much more volume than the terrestrial planets and there is much more material in them. But they are only about one fourth as dense as the terrestrial planets. If you could thoroughly mix the material out of which the earth and Jupiter are made, a pint of the earth would be four times as heavy as a pint of Jupiter. The terrestrial planets are made up of more heavy, dense elements than the giant planets, which are evidently composed of a larger proportion of the lighter elements. The giant planets are covered by a dense cloud-laden atmosphere perhaps a hundred miles or so in depth. We have never seen their solid surfaces.

It seems utterly impossible that there can be life upon the giant planets. If there is life in the solar system we must look for it upon the terrestrial planets, and even upon these bodies which bear some resemblance to the earth the outlook for life as we know it is certainly not bright.

▶ How do the inner planets appear to move in the sky?

By the inner planets we mean Mercury and Venus, the planets which revolve inside the orbit of the earth, between the earth and the sun. Let us consider, for example, the motion of Venus (which will serve for Mercury also; there is no essential difference between them except that Mercury moves much faster). Suppose we start when Venus first begins to become visible as it moves out from behind the sun as at V_1 in Figure 46. As seen in the sky, it appears a little east of the sun, a bright star going down a little after the sun in the evening. Venus moves slowly away from the sun toward the east, so that each day it sets a little later than the sun, until after some 220 days it is about forty-six degrees away at V_2, when—seen through a telescope—it would appear like the moon at first quarter.

Venus now begins to swing in between the earth and sun, moving toward the sun much more rapidly than it moved away from

47. After Venus vanishes in front of the sun in the western sky it emerges as a thin crescent in the morning sky in the east.

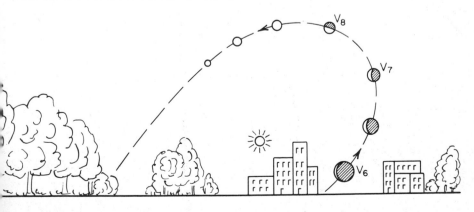

it before, since now it is on the near side of the sun instead of the far side. During this time Venus shows a crescent phase through a telescope because only a small portion of the illuminated disk is visible to the earth. While the fraction of the disk illuminated is steadily shrinking, the disk itself appears to grow larger, as the planet approaches the earth. The result is that Venus reaches its greatest brightness when it appears as a rather fat crescent at V_3. Venus is now moving westward while the sun, as always, is moving eastward. The result is the two seem to be rushing together in the sky, so that unless you watch carefully Venus goes through the phases at V_4 and V_5 before you know it.

Venus now passes from the eastern to the western side of the sun, as shown in the diagram at V_6, going through the crescent phases in reverse order. The planet rises before the sun as a morning star, attaining its greatest brilliance at V_7 and reaching its greatest apparent distance from the sun at V_8. The planet now moves slowly off, around to the far side of the sun, until it passes behind it, only to reappear once against in the sunset sky as an evening star.

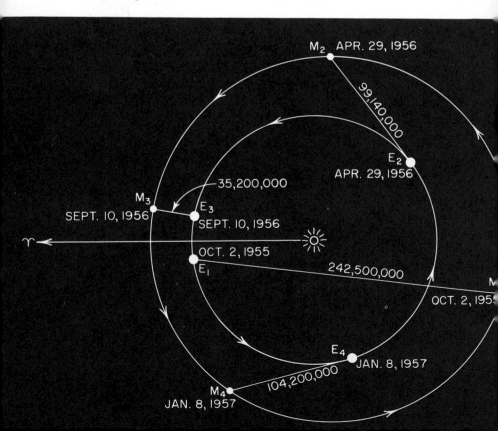

▶ How do the outer planets appear to move in the sky?

Let us consider only the motion of Mars, since the motion of the other outer planets is so similar that a discussion of one will do for all. We will begin when Mars is on the far side of the sun as at M_1 in Figure 48. Seen in the morning sky, it appears as a star of moderate brightness rising a little before the sun. Both Mars and the sun are moving eastward, but the sun is moving eastward considerably faster, with the result that the distance between them increases steadily. Mars moves out from behind the sun until it is a quarter of the way around the sky or 90° west of the sun at M_2, when it is said to be at western quadrature. You are not likely to see Mars in this position because you would have to get up so early in the morning to do so.

Mars now begins to move around in back of the earth, so to speak, getting so far away from the sun that presently you can see it rising before midnight. As Mars approaches the point at which it is opposite the sun in the sky its eastward motion begins to slow down until finally it comes to a full stop as at M_2' in Figure 49. Then it starts to move in the opposite direction among the stars, or toward the west. It moves westward fastest at the time the earth passes the planet in its orbit when it is just opposite the sun at M_3, and appropriately said to be in opposition. You may now see Mars rising in the east about the same time the sun is setting in the west. This apparent backward or westward motion of Mars among the stars was a sore puzzle to the old astronomers, who thought the planets revolved around the earth, in which case there was no reason for them to back up in their orbits. To explain it they had to introduce an extra circular motion for the outer planets which never did work satisfactorily. Mars (and the other outer planets) appear to retrograde for a while among the stars for the same reason an automobile appears to be drifting backward when you pass it, or for the same reason that when you are in a train nearby objects seem to move backward, compared with the landscape in the distance. As the earth approaches and passes, Mars

48. Relative position of Mars and earth in 1955, 1956, and 1957. Numbers show distance apart in miles.

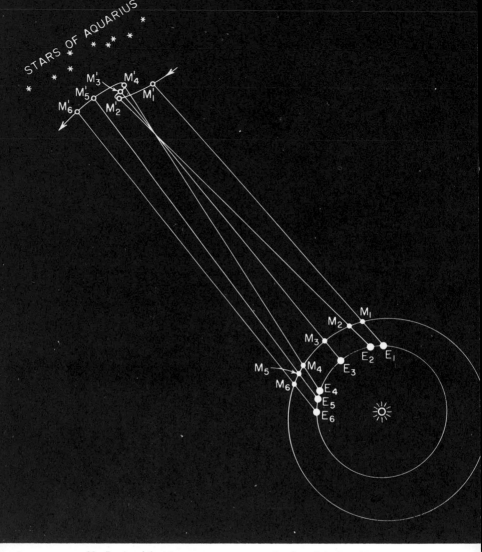

49. For a while Mars appears to move backward in its orbit as earth passes the planet. The apparent motion of Mars is seen against the background of stars.

seems to move backward compared with the stars, which show no motion owing to their immensely greater distance.

After passing opposition, Mars' westward motion slows down until it reaches its second stationary point at M_4'. Now it is considerably past the point of opposition, so far that the motion of the earth is no longer sufficient to give the planet any westward motion in relation to the stars. The result is that once again Mars starts moving slowly eastward.

Mars is now moving away from the sun but its eastward motion is slower than that of the sun. There comes a day when Mars is at eastern quadrature at M_4. Mars may now be seen directly south in the sky at sunset. The sun is moving eastward much more rapidly than Mars and finally overtakes it. The process begins to repeat as Mars slowly emerges from behind the sun into the morning sky.

▶ Why do the planets show phases?

Mercury and Venus show phases like those of the moon, from a thin crescent to full. This is caused by the fact that when they come directly between the sun and the earth, only their unilluminated side is turned earthward and we are unable to see them or we see only a thin crescent disk. Then, as the planet moves farther from the line joining the earth and sun, we see more of the illuminated surface, until we see the planet in the same way that we see the moon quarter phase. After that, the planet begins to move around in back of the sun so that we begin to see more than a quarter of the whole disk illuminated. Finally when the planet is around on the far side of the sun we may see all (or nearly all) of the illuminated disk. The planet is usually a little above or below the line joining the earth and sun so that we seldom see *all* of the night side or *all* of the illuminated side.

▶ Why don't the outer planets show phases?

Actually they *do* show phases but not nearly as much as the inner planets do. This is because an outer planet can never come between the earth and the sun, as an inner planet does. Mars shows some phase all the time except when directly opposite the sun at opposition, when of course it must be at the full phase. When Mars is 90° east or west of the sun the planet appears to be

113

gibbous, resembling the disk of the moon about three days before or after the full phase. Even Jupiter shows a little phase which is too slight to be easily noticed, although it has to be taken into account when making precise measurements on the planet. Saturn, Uranus, and Neptune are so distant that they do not show a perceptible phase.

▶ Which planet comes nearest the earth?

The moon, of course, is the planet nearest to the earth. We also know of some minor planets (asteroids) that may come almost as close to the earth as the moon does. Aside from these, Venus comes much closer to the earth than any other celestial body. A close approach of Venus occurs when it comes between the earth and sun. At such times the distance of Venus from the earth is reduced to about 25 million miles, 100 times the distance of the moon. Such close approaches are not of much help in observing Venus since at that time the night side of Venus is turned toward the earth, so that we are unable to see the planet at all, or at most only a thin sliver of light.

▶ How close can Mars come to the earth?

Mars is closest to the earth when it is directly opposite the sun in the sky. This happens about every two years but the distance of Mars at such times varies greatly, depending upon where the earth passes the planet in its orbit. *On the average,* the planet is 50 million miles away when the earth passes it. The greatest distance occurs when the earth passes Mars at a time the planet is farthest from the sun; Mars and the earth are then separated by as much as 62 million miles.

The minimum distance occurs when the earth passes Mars at a time the planet is at the point in its orbit nearest the sun. These exceptionally close approaches occur at intervals of 15 or 17 years. They always occur in August and September, since the earth passes the point on the orbit of Mars nearest the sun about this time of year. One of the closest approaches of Mars on record occurred in 1924, when on August 22 the earth passed Mars at a distance of only 34,600,000 miles.

The closest approach possible would occur if the earth should

114

pass Mars at a time when earth is *farthest* from the sun and, at the same time, Mars is *nearest* the sun. This cannot happen now since the point on the orbit of the earth farthest from the sun (aphelion), is turned far away from the perihelion point of the orbit of Mars. But after thousands of years, as the result of the disturbing action of the other planets on the orbits of both Mars and the earth, the aphelion point on the orbit of the earth will lie in the same direction in space as the perihelion of the orbit of Mars. The distance separating the two planets will then be reduced to an absolute minimum of 33,800,000 miles. But by that time we will probably have made the trip to Mars, so this closeness will be of little advantage to us.

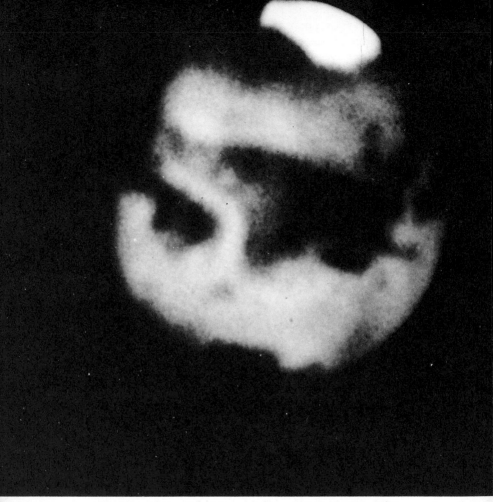

50. Mars, photographed in red light on August 10, 1956. White area is south polar cap. Dark regions are "seas" or maria, light regions are deserts. Red light is penetrating and shows surface markings.

116

7 ▶ A CLOSE-UP OF SOME ，
OF THE PLANETS

▶ *Questions on Mars*

Let us imagine a conversation between an astronomer and a visitor to an observatory. Mars is supposed to be only about 40 million miles from the earth, close enough so that the surface markings on its disk are clearly visible. The astronomer and visitor are studying the planet with a large telescope of the type known as a reflector, which uses a mirror instead of a lens to bring the light to a focus.

ASTRONOMER (*adjusting eyepiece on telescope*). There . . . now take a look at Mars and tell me what you see.

VISITOR (*peering into eyepiece*). I see a reddish-colored disk with some bluish-gray markings on it, and a white spot at the top. What are they?

ASTRONOMER. The reddish areas seem to be nothing but vast deserts of bare ground that cover about 60 per cent of the planet's surface. The darker bluish-gray markings like those on the moon are called *maria,* or seas. The white spot is the south polar cap.

VISITOR. Are there really seas on Mars?

ASTRONOMER. Before about 1877 astronomers thought the dark markings actually were seas and oceans. For this reason they considered Mars a planet very much like the earth. Now we feel sure the entire surface of Mars, except a little around the polar caps, is dry land.

VISITOR. How do you know it isn't water?

ASTRONOMER. If there were great expanses of water on Mars we would see the bright reflection of the sun in them. Even a small body of water like a lake would show a bright reflection, but nothing of the sort has ever been observed. Also, the maria often show a detailed structure we would not expect to find in a sea or ocean unless it was very shallow. On most drawings and photographs the maria appear flat and smooth, but when atmospheric conditions are very good they resemble masses of twisted ribbon, as if they did not cover the surface solidly at all.

VISITOR. What do you think the maria are?

ASTRONOMER. The appearance of the maria changes with the Martian seasons in a way that leads us to think they may be due to vegetation. During the Martian winter they are dim and their borders poorly defined. But as spring comes on they show a change. As the polar cap—

VISITOR. By the way, what is the polar cap?

ASTRONOMER. We believe the polar cap is a thin deposit of snow and frost, possibly only a couple of inches deep. It spreads over a great deal of surface but it is extremely thin. We used to think the Martian polar cap was composed of frozen carbon dioxide gas or dry ice, but that idea has now been abandoned. The temperature on Mars does not seem to be low enough for carbon dioxide to freeze. Also, the polar caps reflect light in the same way that snow does, not like dry ice.

VISITOR. So the polar caps of Mars consist of frozen water?

ASTRONOMER. We have every reason to believe so.

VISITOR. Now what happens as the polar cap begins to shrink in the spring?

ASTRONOMER. As the polar cap begins to shrink, the maria around it turn darker. This darkening spreads toward the equator at the rate of about 28 miles per day. It finally reaches the equator and even goes over into the opposite hemisphere.

VISITOR. What do you think is happening?

ASTRONOMER. It looks as if vegetation were springing up, brought to life by moisture from the polar cap.

VISITOR. You mean water from the polar cap runs down over the planet—

ASTRONOMER. No. No. Nothing like that. The water could not flow down over the surface of Mars from the polar cap to the equator, any more than water from the snows of Canada could flood the United States. The water at any place on the planet is in equilibrium with the force of gravity there and the centrifugal

118

51. Valley below Mt. Wilson, photographed in violet light. Violet light is not penetrating and so does not show mountains in distance. Neither does violet light penetrate the atmosphere of Mars.

52. Valley below Mt. Wilson, photographed in red light. Red light pierces the atmospheric haze and shows mountains in distance. Red light similarly pierces the atmosphere of Mars.

force, due to rotation. To make water move any distance you would have to force it over the ground by pumping.

VISITOR. Then how does the water get over the surface?

ASTRONOMER. There is probably very little water in liquid form around the polar cap. In the thin atmosphere of Mars it is believed that the moisture goes directly into the air by evaporation. Then this moisture is carried over the planet as a dry gas by atmospheric circulation.

VISITOR. So the maria are supposed to consist of vegetation?

ASTRONOMER. That seems like the most natural explanation of the seasonal darkening we see in the spring. Also, the maria have the power of regeneration. Occasionally we observe what are apparently great dust storms on Mars. Now suppose that the maria

53. Mt. San Antonio, photographed in red light. Green plants absorb red light, hence trees in foreground appear dark.

54. Mt. San Antonio, photographed in infrared light. Green plants reflect infrared light strongly, hence trees in foreground appear bright.

were simply darker regions on the surface of the planet. After only a short time they would be covered by dust until the whole planet was a uniform reddish brown. Instead, the maria come out strong each Martian spring. It looks as if they must be due to some substance that has the power to come alive each year.

VISITOR. What kind of plants could they be?

ASTRONOMER. That is what we would like to know. The plants here on earth that would be most likely to survive on Mars are the lichens, especially the crustose type that you often see growing as scales on rocks and old monuments. These are the hardiest plants known on earth. They can survive extreme heat and cold. They grow on the desert, on high mountaintops, or in caves at sea level. You can immerse them in liquid air and they will still

121

go on living. It is possible they might even be able to survive the rigors of the Martian climate.

VISITOR. So the maria consist of lichens?

ASTRONOMER. I didn't say that. There are objections to such an idea. Lichens show no such seasonal changes as the maria do. Also, they grow *very* slowly, so slowly that often it is hard to tell whether they are dead or alive. But the maria often show considerable change in a comparatively short time. For example, in 1954 there was a dark area the size of Texas—which had developed from practically nothing in less than two years. Furthermore, lichens grow so sparsely that they never lend any particular color to the landscape. They are extremely patchy in their growth. The maria, on the other hand, appear to be fairly well covered. The idea of lichens on Mars seems to have been overemphasized.

VISITOR. Maybe they aren't plants at all.

ASTRONOMER. There is observational evidence that they consist of some kind of living organic substance. This is hard to explain in a few words, but if you examine any kind of organic substance (such as a leaf or piece of living tissue) by infrared light far beyond the range of sensitivity of the eye, you will find that it shows a dark absorption band that can be revealed by suitable instruments sensitive to this kind of radiation. There is evidence for the presence of this absorption band in the light of Mars, indicating the presence of organic life on the planet.

VISITOR. Maybe the maria are just big prairies covered with grass.

ASTRONOMER. We can perform an elementary experiment that shows the maria cannot be covered by green vegetation containing chlorophyll like grass or the green foliage of trees. Take a look at this photograph of Mount San Antonio, a ten-thousand-foot peak, fifty miles from the Mount Wilson Observatory. (Fig. 53) What I want you to notice particularly is the green trees in the foreground.

VISITOR. What about them?

ASTRONOMER. This photograph was taken in deep red light. Notice how dark the foliage on the trees looks in the picture. (Fig. 53) That is because green vegetation reflects red light very poorly. When you look at grass and green trees through a red filter they appear almost black. Now take a look at this photograph. (Fig. 54)

122

VISITOR. It looks as if the trees are covered with snow. How was it taken?

ASTRONOMER. This photograph was taken within a few minutes of the other one but in *infrared* light—light just a little bit beyond the range of sensitivity of the eye. The chlorophyll in green vegetation reflects infrared light powerfully. That is what produces the "snowfall" effect. The green foliage reflects the infrared light so strongly that it comes out overexposed and looks white.

VISITOR. What has this got to do with Mars?

ASTRONOMER. Suppose we take a photograph of Mars in red light and then in infrared light. Now if the maria *are* covered by green vegetation they should look dark on the red photograph as they do to the eye. But on the infrared photograph they should look bright—possibly as bright as the deserts around them.

VISITOR. That's right! It should be a sure test for chlorophyll.

ASTRONOMER. Here is the dismal result of such an experiment. These are photographs of Mars taken a few minutes apart in red light and infrared light. (Figs. 55 and 56.)

VISITOR. They look pretty much the same to me.

ASTRONOMER. That's right. The maria look dark in *both* red and infrared light.

VISITOR. Then there can't be any chlorophyll in the maria— they're not green plants.

ASTRONOMER. There is one possible loophole. The Russians have made some interesting observations on the way plants reflect light in the very cold dry climate of the Pamir plateau under practically Martian conditions. They find that plants growing in these cold climates have foliage that is much bluer than that of the same plants growing in temperate climates. You might say that they absorb nearly all the radiation of the sun falling upon them except light in the green, blue, and violet regions of the spectrum. They do this as a matter of protection against the extreme cold. By absorbing more sunlight they tend to keep themselves warmer. Plants in temperate climates only absorb in the red. It may be significant that the maria have a bluish tinge. They are often described as green but this is probably due to an optical effect in the lens-type telescopes with which most of the observations of Mars have been made. In a mirror-type telescope—in which this effect is not present—the maria have a decided bluish-gray tint,

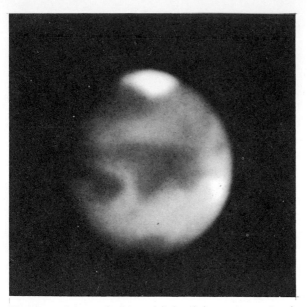

55. Mars, photographed in red light. If the maria consist of vegetation like terrestrial plants they should appear dark.

56. Mars, photographed in infrared light. If the maria consist of green vegetation like that on earth they should come up bright. Instead they look the same in both red and infrared light.

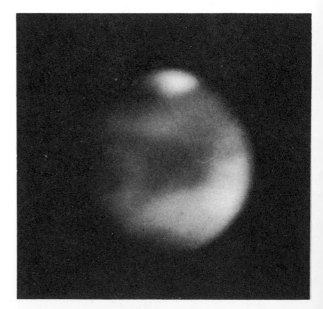

124

observed when Mars was close in 1956 and 1958.

VISITOR. What could the maria be if they do not consist of vegetation?

ASTRONOMER. It has been suggested that they may be some kind of mineral that changes tint due to moisture. But there is so little moisture in the atmosphere of Mars that it seems doubtful if it could have much effect. The whole question of the changes in the maria is still far from answered. The maria change appearance with the seasons in a way that suggests the growth and decay of vegetation. Yet plants on the earth require oxygen for their growth, and there is no evidence of oxygen on Mars. If the maria are covered by vegetation it must be of an entirely different type from that known to us. Instead of looking for plants on Mars similar to those on the earth, or plants that have adapted themselves to Martian conditions, perhaps we should expect to find plants of an entirely different type than those familiar to us. In any case, it would seem that the biologist would have a bigger stake in a trip to Mars than the astronomer.

VISITOR. You say there is no oxygen in the atmosphere of Mars. What does its atmosphere consist of, then?

ASTRONOMER. Our best guess is that the atmosphere of Mars is like that of the earth, but with the oxygen left out. This means that it consists mostly of nitrogen gas with a little argon and carbon dioxide. These gases are not poisonous—we breath them on earth all the time—but they will not support life. They are dead: inactive, inert. The Martian atmosphere, even at the surface of the planet, is also very thin. It is estimated to be about the same density as that in our atmosphere at an altitude of 60,000 feet.

VISITOR. What about the temperature of Mars?

ASTRONOMER. Since Mars is half again as far from the sun as the earth we would expect it to be quite cold. This belief is borne out by actual measures of its surface heat.

VISITOR. How can you possibly measure the temperature of a body millions of miles away?

ASTRONOMER. It's not easy. We can't very well do it with a thermometer, the way we measure temperatures on the earth. We have to do it with an instrument, very sensitive to heat radiation, called the *thermocouple*. Imagine you had a large rock which you heated until it was white-hot. Suppose you were blindfolded and

125

led to within a few feet of the rock. You could tell it must be quite hot from the heat on your face. The rock then cools until it is red-hot. You would know its temperature is lower since it gives off less heat. The rock cools still farther until it no longer glows but gives out enough heat to be felt at a distance. You could make a rough guess at the temperature of the rock from the intensity of the heat on your face.

The thermocouple is vastly more sensitive to heat radiation than your face is. Basically, it consists of two wires of different metals fused together, usually bismuth and an alloy of bismuth and tin. The fused metals form a target hardly bigger than the head of a pin which is placed at the focus of a large telescope. When light from a star or planet is focused on the junction of the metals it causes a current of electricity to flow through them. The more radiation falls on the thermocouple, the stronger this current becomes. Corrections have to be made for the planetary heat absorbed in our atmosphere. Then, from the laws of radiation the temperature of the surface of the planet can be calculated. The thermocouple is so sensitive that it can even measure the heat radiated from a *cold* spot like the polar cap of Mars.

VISITOR. What kind of temperatures do you find for Mars?

ASTRONOMER. Pretty low. At noon on the equator the temperature rises slightly above freezing—maybe to 45° F. The highest temperature comes at noon or shortly afterward, instead of about three in the afternoon as on the earth. There is no water vapor in the atmosphere to exert a blanketing effect and prevent radiation escaping from the surface. By sunset the temperature has fallen to about 9° F. We cannot measure the temperature at Martian midnight, since the unilluminated side of the planet is never turned toward the earth, but it must reach some very low value. The minimum night temperature on Mars has been estimated as −150° F. Measures on the polar cap give a temperature of −90° F.

VISITOR. Doesn't sound very comfortable.

ASTRONOMER. It is hard to see how animal life could exactly thrive under such conditions—no oxygen, very little water, and an intensely cold climate.

VISITOR. What about those canals?

ASTRONOMER. Take a look through the telescope.

126

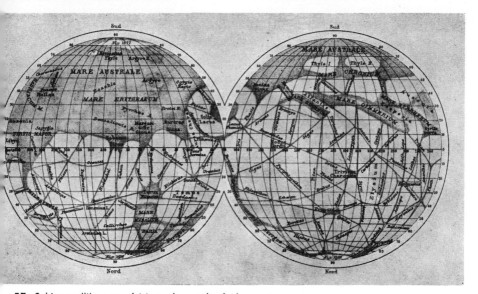

57. Schiaparelli's map of Mars, the result of observations that extended from 1877 to 1888. Schiaparelli was first to see canals on Mars.

VISITOR (*peering into eyepiece*). I can't see anything that looks like a canal.

ASTRONOMER. You would have to be very lucky to see canals on your first try. Conditions have to be just right. Mars has to be fairly close to the earth—less than about 50 million miles. Then the season on Mars has to be right. The best time to see canals is when it is spring and early summer in the southern hemisphere. In the fall and winter you seldom get a good look at them.

VISITOR. How long have the canals been known?

ASTRONOMER. They were discovered in 1877 by an Italian astronomer named Giovanni Schiaparelli. Mars came within 35 million miles of the earth that year—an exceptionally close approach—and Schiaparelli made the most of it. He had a telescope with only an 8-inch glass in the end, but he was an experienced planetary observer and he worked under the calm Italian skies. In seeing canals the steadiness of the atmosphere is much more important than a large telescope.

VISITOR. So what happened?

ASTRONOMER. As a result of his observations that year Schiaparelli produced a map of Mars that was different from any astronomers had ever seen before. It showed the deserts crossed by many lines, or maybe narrow stripes would be a better term. Schiaparelli called these stripes *canali,* which in Italian means "channels."

VISITOR. Channels? Did he really think—

ASTRONOMER. Apparently he merely used the word as a sort of shorthand term while working at the telescope. He might have called them boulevards. He had to call them something.

VISITOR. So that's the way it was.

ASTRONOMER. The trouble was that *canali* was translated into English not as "channels" but as "canals." Now, in English *canal* implies an artificial waterway constructed by intelligent beings. Immediately there was great excitement, for canals meant that there was intelligent life on Mars. And the excitement has never died down.

VISITOR. But couldn't other astronomers see the canals?

ASTRONOMER. Not at first. Schiaparelli came in for a good deal of criticism. But apparently it didn't bother him, for when Mars came fairly close again in 1879 he produced another map of Mars which showed even more canals than before—and worse still, some of them were *double.* That is, there were two canals running side by side for hundreds of miles like a railroad track.

VISITOR. Sounds incredible.

ASTRONOMER. That's what a lot of astronomers thought, too. It was a long time before anyone could see canals on Mars besides Schiaparelli. Not until 1886 did confirmation come; that year they were sighted by both Perrotin in Vienna and H. C. Wilson at Cincinnati. When Mars was again close, in 1892, the best results so far were obtained with the 36-inch telescope at the Lick Observatory. Yet other experienced observers—working with equally fine telescopes—were unable to see so much as a single canal and were naturally highly skeptical of their existence.

VISITOR. Can't say I blame them.

ASTRONOMER. You can hardly expect to be lucky enough to see the canals the first few times you look. The seeing conditions have to be very good or the canals do not appear. That is what has happened to astronomers so often. They have looked a few times when the seeing was fairly good and concluded that there was nothing to see. But you have to be persistent. Fine seeing is much the most essential factor in bringing out the canals. In my opinion, there has been too much hocus-pocus, too much mystery, made of the canals on Mars. It does not require a particular kind of eye to make them out, only really fine seeing conditions.

VISITOR. What's the matter with tonight?

ASTRONOMER. Well, the seeing is only fair. Occasionally I can catch a glimpse of a canal but then I know exactly where to look. When you have really wonderful seeing, when the air is so still the image of Mars stands out like an engraving, then not just a few canals but the whole canal pattern may flash out. It is visible only for four or five seconds at the most. Apparently Percival Lowell was the first astronomer in the United States to see the whole canal pattern at once.

VISITOR. Lowell believed there are real canals on Mars, didn't he?

ASTRONOMER. That's right. As a result of his observations he became convinced that the canals are actual waterways constructed by the Martians for the purpose of bringing water from the melting polar cap down over the dry surface of the planet for irrigation purposes. We do not see the canals themselves, which are too narrow to be visible from this distance, but rather the vegetation growing along their borders. The existence of a worldwide canal system implies not only a high type of intelligence but a civilization in which national boundaries have been wiped out in the universal desire for that one essential of life—water.

VISITOR. Sounds reasonable.

ASTRONOMER. It is an ingenious idea which is undeniably attractive, almost too attractive, in fact. I rather regret to say that no astronomer of any standing believes it today. Unfortunately, it's just altogether too farfetched in our present state of ignorance.

VISITOR. You must have some notion about the nature of the canals yourself.

ASTRONOMER. It is my personal opinion that they are simply narrow extensions of the maria into the deserts. That is the way they look to me and that is the way Schiaparelli and other Martian observers have drawn them. They also convey to me the impression

129

of being some natural surface feature. When I have seen them they were the same color as the maria.

VISITOR. But what sort of *natural* surface feature could resemble the canals?

ASTRONOMER. Possibly the maria and the canals are all part of one big mass of vegetation embracing the whole planet. The canals may be runners or creepers extending from the maria over the deserts and connecting with the round spots or oases. We see such "canals" on a very small scale in the runners and creepers extending from strawberry and ivy vines in our gardens.

VISITOR. They're not as exciting as canals constructed by intelligent beings.

ASTRONOMER. Maybe if we can establish an observatory on the moon where we will always have perfect seeing we can get the answer. Or maybe we can get the answer from a rocket probe that goes near the surface of a planet and sends back information about it. Or maybe men will actually have to land on Mars before we solve the mystery of the canals. (*Peering into telescope.*) Hello! One of the moons of Mars just popped into view. Take a look.

VISITOR. You mean that little star alongside Mars?

ASTRONOMER. That's it. It wasn't there a few minutes ago. Let me see which one it is. I'll have to look it up in the *American Ephemeris and Nautical Almanac*. It's the official publication, put out by the Naval Observatory, which gives the positions of all the planets and their satellites. Ah . . . here it is. That is Phobos we see in the telescope. It is the nearer moon, the one that moves so fast.

VISITOR. I think it's moved a little just since we've been talking about it.

ASTRONOMER. Wouldn't be surprised. Phobos revolves around Mars in about seven hours. We can see it move from one side of the planet to the other and back again in the course of a single night.

VISITOR. I had always supposed the moons of Mars would be hard to see, but this one is quite easy.

ASTRONOMER. The two little moons of Mars are so easily seen you wonder why they were so long in being discovered.

VISITOR. When were they discovered?

ASTRONOMER. In 1877, the same year Mars' canals were discovered, by an astronomer at the Naval Observatory named Asaph Hall. The Naval Observatory had just installed a new 26-inch refracting telescope which Hall planned to use in his search for a moon of Mars that year. Hall said he undertook the search because he was tired of reading in textbooks that "Mars has no moons."

VISITOR. So he found them both?

ASTRONOMER. He looked for many nights without finding a trace even of one. Finally he gave up and went home from the observatory feeling completely discouraged. But his wife apparently had more faith in her husband than he had in himself, for she urged him to return to the observatory for one more look. So he went back and had only searched around Mars a few minutes when he found an object that looked more hopeful than anything he had seen so far. He barely had time to measure its position when a fog came in from the Potomac and put a stop to observations.

VISITOR. Why does it have to happen like that?

ASTRONOMER. The fog continued for several nights. When Hall finally got another look at Mars, he not only confirmed his earlier discovery but also found another object that moved with such bewildering rapidity that at first he thought Mars must have several

58. Orbits of the moons of Mars—Phobos and Deimos—around the planet.

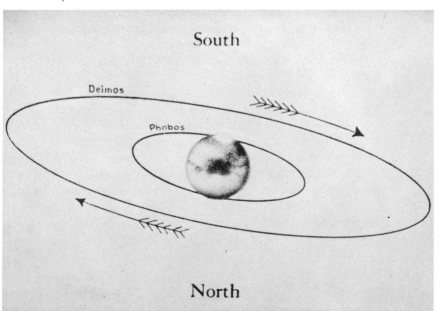

moons. Finally by keeping watch all night he established that there were only two moons, but one was so close to Mars and moved around the planet so fast that it was hard to keep track of it. He named the inner moon *Phobos* (Fear) and the outer one *Deimos* (Panic), after the two companions of the war god Mars.

VISITOR. They move around Mars like artificial satellites.

ASTRONOMER. The strange ways of an artificial satellite would be no novelty to Martians: Phobos goes around Mars three times while Mars is rotating once on its axis. As seen from Mars, Phobos would rise in the west and set in the east twice in a single day, the interval between one rising and the next being 11 hours. But the time between rising and setting would be only 4 hours 18 minutes, since the satellite revolves so close to the surface that it cannot be seen throughout a whole revolution.

VISITOR. How about Deimos?

ASTRONOMER. Deimos would rise in the east and set in the west in the way we are accustomed to seeing a moon behave. But since it revolves around Mars only a little more slowly than it takes Mars to rotate on its axis, Deimos would appear to move across the sky at a very leisurely pace, so that there would be five and a half days between two consecutive risings of Deimos. If it went around Mars at exactly the same rate that Mars rotates then of course it would never rise or set, but would always hover over the same place on the planet.

VISITOR. How large are these moons of Mars?

ASTRONOMER. Their size can only be estimated from the amount of light they reflect, so it is pretty uncertain. Phobos is estimated to be about ten miles in diameter and Deimos about five. Mere mountains hurtling through space.

VISITOR. When will Mars be close to the earth again?

ASTRONOMER. The earth passes Mars at intervals of about two years and two months; of course the planet is fairly close at each passage. But the distance varies considerably depending upon whether we pass the planet when it is in a part of its orbit close to the sun or one that is far away. Mars is going to be at a considerable distance from the earth for quite a while to come. Not until 1971 will Mars make one of its exceptionally close approaches to the earth, but this will be an awfully good one. In fact, on August 6, 1971, Mars will be at just about the minimum distance from the earth it is possible to come. Here are dates at which the earth will pass Mars in its orbit:

Date	Distance (miles)
Dec. 29, 1960	56,300,000
Feb. 3, 1963	61,900,000
Mar. 8, 1965	61,900,000
Apr. 13, 1967	56,300,000
May 29, 1969	45,400,000
Aug. 6, 1971	34,700,000
Oct. 21, 1973	40,100,000
Dec. 13, 1975	52,500,000

▶ How does Venus look through a telescope?

Venus is most disappointing viewed through a telescope. The planet has the provoking trait of promising a great deal but giving very little. She looks exciting—as a bright star viewed by the eye. But in a telescope you see only a blank white disk devoid of surface markings. Markings have been seen on Venus, but not very often. There is evidence that viewing Venus through a blue filter helps in this respect. As we shall see presently, markings can almost always be photographed on Venus in invisible ultraviolet light, well beyond the eye's range of sensitivity. The markings on Venus seem to show in greater contrast in blue, violet, and ultraviolet light than in yellow, orange, or red light, the colors to which the eye is most sensitive.

▶ Why does Venus look so much brighter than the other planets?

For two reasons. One is that Venus comes so much closer to the earth than any other planet. The other is that the surface of Venus is covered by clouds which are very good reflectors of sunlight. As a result, even when Venus is in a part of its orbit far from the earth, it still appears brighter than any other planet. Farthest away from the earth, its disk is small and appears like that of the moon near the full phase. As it moves out from behind the sun we see less of the illuminated part of the disk, but the disk as a whole gets larger, since the planet is approaching the

133

earth. This increase in size of the disk more than makes up for the decrease in the extent of the illuminated portion. Maximum brightness is reached a little after passing the quarter phase, when the planet appears as a rather fat crescent in a telescope—like the moon when it is five days old. At such a time Venus is easily visible in the daytime if you have good eyesight and know just where to look. At night, if there is no moon and no artificial light around, the planet shines brightly enough to cast a distinct shadow. It is worth looking for, and you are likely to get quite a thrill out of seeing planet shadows for the first time.

▶ *What kind of a world is Venus?*

Although Venus comes closer to the earth than any other planet except the moon, we still know very little about it. This is because the planet guards its secrets very closely within the clouds that perpetually cover its surface. We could make a much better guess at the nature of conditions on the surface of Venus if we only knew for sure what makes up the cloud layer.

Back in the early part of this century astronomers felt sure they knew what the Venusian clouds were. They were clouds of water vapor like those we see floating overhead above the earth. If this were the case, then Venus must be a decidedly watery world to produce a cloud cover that *never* breaks to reveal the surface below. And since Venus is nearer the sun than the earth it must be quite hot beneath the cloud layer. This gave rise to a picture of Venus as a steaming, watery world covered with swamps and oceans something like the earth during the mushier periods of its history. Artists painted imaginative scenes of conditions on Venus, generally depicting some animal crawling out of the ocean, with clouds hovering overhead, and plants around that looked suspiciously like those that grew on the earth during the Carboniferous Age.

As early as 1923 some doubts as to the validity of this form of Venusian landscape arose when observers at Mount Wilson were unable to detect evidence for water vapor lines in the spectrum of Venus. The fact that such lines could not be detected did not rule out the presence of water completely. The spectrograph can only detect water in the form of an invisible vapor. It cannot detect it in

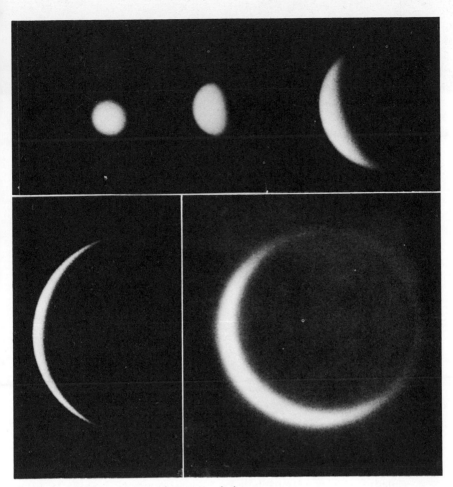

59. Phases of Venus, showing relative size of planet at
different distances from the sun. Largest image was taken
when Venus was between earth and sun.

135

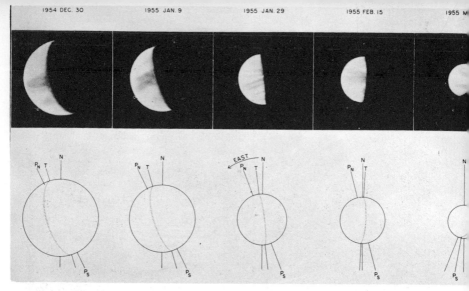

60. *Above:* Drawings of photographs of Venus taken in ultraviolet light. Diagrams below indicate position of planet's axis of rotation as determined from image of January 29, 1955.

61. *Right:* Venus always shows dark cloud belts when photographed in ultraviolet light. Photographs indicate rapid changes from day to day in Venusian atmosphere.

the form of clouds or ice particles. But later, when further research was made for spectrum lines of water vapor by more powerful instruments with the same negative results, considerable doubt was thrown on the presence of large bodies of water on Venus.* But if the clouds were not composed of water vapor, what were they? There are very few substances known likely to produce clouds essentially white in color like those on Venus. The only gas so far identified in the atmosphere of Venus is carbon dioxide, the same gas that comes bubbling out of soda water when you open a bottle. Carbon-dioxide gas is very abundant in the atmosphere of Venus, possibly five hundred times as abundant as in our own atmosphere. But carbon dioxide by itself cannot account for the white-cloud cover.

The inability of astronomers to detect water vapor in the atmosphere of Venus led to a radically different picture of the planet

* Since this was written water vapor has been detected in the atmosphere of Venus from balloon flights.

136

from that in vogue earlier. Overnight Venus was changed to a dustbowl planet. The slight lemonish tint of the clouds was accounted for by dust thrown up from deserts which were presumed to be of a tawny color. But still this left the question of the cloud layer open.

Recently we have had a return to the old water-vapor hypothesis, although for somewhat different reasons than those originally proposed. The problem is to account for the great abundance of carbon dioxide.

Suppose originally there were large amounts of carbon dioxide gas thrown into the atmosphere from volcanoes. On the earth this gas has combined with the surface rocks to form limestone and other substances, so that today vast quantities of fossil carbon dioxide are locked in the rocks of this planet. But the abundance of carbon dioxide in the atmosphere of Venus indicates that carbon dioxide has not combined with the surface rocks there. Venus is a

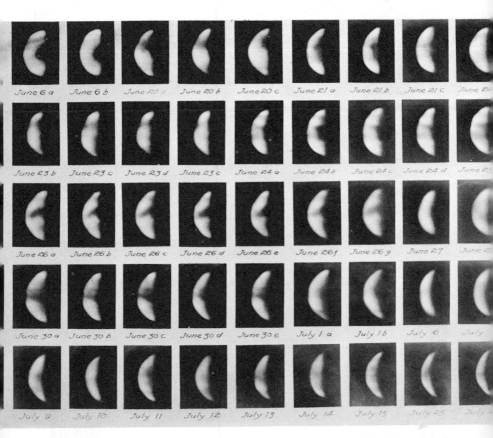

planet about the size of the earth. What could have caused the difference?

A possible answer has been proposed by F. L. Whipple and D. H. Menzel of the Harvard College Observatory. They point out that if Venus is *entirely* covered by water there will be no opportunity for carbonates to form, since there is no land in contact with the atmosphere. And after the surface layer of the ocean had become saturated with carbon dioxide—so that a "buffer" layer was formed—no more would go into solution. The clouds are therefore just what they appear to be—water vapor. The inability of our instruments to detect water vapor above the cloud layer is attributed to the fact that there is very little present in the form of a gas. Measures with the thermocouple give a temperature of $-40°$ F. for the visible surface of Venus. If this temperature refers to the visible cloud layer, then whatever water is present would be in the form of ice crystals or water droplets—to which the spectrograph is blind. The idea of having the planet completely covered by water naturally accounts for the cloud cover as well as supplying an explanation for the abundance of carbon dioxide. On the whole, the universal-ocean hypothesis sounds quite plausible applied to Venus.

▶ What kind of world is Jupiter?

Whether we regard Jupiter from the standpoint of either its bulk or its mass, it is by far the largest of all the planets in the solar system; in fact, it is more massive than all of them put together. Although when it is closest to the earth Jupiter is about ten times as far away as Mars at closest approach, it is so big that it shows a disk in the telescope more than twice the size of Mars. This naturally makes Jupiter one of the most satisfactory objects in the sky for viewing with a small telescope. With only an ordinary 2-inch spyglass it is possible to see the dark cloud belts across the equatorial region of the planet, and with a telescope of 6 inches aperture the disk shows a vast amount of changing detail that makes it a delight to watch. The four major satellites of Jupiter alone would make the planet one of the most interesting objects in the heavens for telescopic study.

Not so many years ago an astronomer who was asked "What

kind of world is Jupiter?" gave an answer entirely different from the one he gives today. In our grandfathers' time Jupiter was considered to be so hot as to be practically self-luminous. Thus Richard A. Proctor of the Royal Astronomical Society, writing in 1870, described the four giant planets Jupiter, Saturn, Uranus, and Neptune as "four suns . . . not indeed suns resplendent like the primary sun around which we travel, yet giving out perhaps no insignificant supply of light; not heated to incandescence . . . but still supplying an amount of heat proportionally far greater than the quantity of light they give forth . . . in such sort that the small worlds which circle them are provided with all that is necessary for the well being of their inhabitants." (It is rather curious to note how astronomers of another day seemed to take for granted that there was life on other worlds, while today we are exceedingly skeptical of there being life on any of the planets except our own. The possibility of life on other worlds seems to decrease as our knowledge of them increases.) As late as 1918 we find in Young's *Lessons in Astronomy,* a standard text of that time, ". . . many things in [Jupiter's] appearance indicate a *high temperature. . . .* In short, it appears very probable that the planet is a sort of *semi-sun*—hot, though not so hot as to be self-luminous."

Then Sir Harold Jeffreys demonstrated in 1923 that very little heat could be issuing from beneath the solid surface. Even if the crust were very poorly conducting, enough time must have elapsed for the surface to have solidified completely unless the interior contained an improbably high amount of radioactive material. Shortly after Jeffreys' theoretical conclusions were published, actual measures of the heat radiation from the surface of Jupiter with the thermocouple gave a temperature of −210° F. The planet is far from being a semi-sun; the temperature at the surface was as low as some substances exhibited as curiosities, such as liquid air.

Jupiter is always covered by cloud belts so that we never see the planet's solid surface. While its general appearance is the same due to the cloud belts crossing its disk, these cloud belts change continually and exhibit a bewildering amount of detail within them. The numerous markings on Jupiter make it easy to determine the planet's rotation period. As it turns out, however, Jupiter does not rotate as a solid body but has different rotation periods in

139

62. Jupiter, photographed in blue light showing the Great Red Spot. The appearance of the planet is generally the same but changes in detail from night to night.

different latitudes. This is true also of the sun, but the sun's rate of rotation decreases from equator to poles in a regular way. As for Jupiter, the rotation is fastest at the equator (9 hours 50 minutes 30 seconds), while the rotation outside the equator is 9 hours 55 minutes 41 seconds.

The most famous marking on Jupiter and the only one of a permanent character is that known as the Great Red Spot. Attention was first directed in 1878 to this area, which was then rising to prominence and had not previously been recorded. During the next four years it dominated the surface of the planet because of its size and extent as well as its striking red color. A search of old records revealed that it probably was not a new feature but had only been "discovered" because of a sudden increase in darkness and color. In fact, it appears to have been noticed by such early observers as Robert Hooke in 1664. The first definite drawing we have of the spot has been traced back to one made in 1831 by Schwabe, the same man who discovered the eleven-year sunspot cycle. Since its discovery in 1878 the Red Spot, or at least the place occupied by the Red Spot, has been under continuous observation. The principal features of the Great Red Spot are its tremendous size, about 7000 miles in width by 24,000 miles in length, its oval shape, variable color, variable rotation period, and long life.

▶ What is the Great Red Spot on Jupiter?

This is the question to which astronomers are still trying to find the answer. It certainly is a very puzzling Jovian feature. One might think of it as a high plateau covered by clouds rising out of the solid surface below. But it cannot be anything attached to the solid surface of the planet because of the spot's variable rotation period. The spot has drifted entirely around the planet, having shifted its position by millions of miles. This has given rise to the idea of the Red Spot as a floating island. The hard part is trying to figure out what it is that floats. The atmosphere of Jupiter is believed to consist almost entirely of hydrogen and helium gas in a highly compressed state; the problem is to find something light enough to float in it.

The only consistent hypothesis regarding the nature of the Red Spot is that put forward tentatively by Bertrand M. Peek, a veteran English observer of Jupiter, based upon a suggestion made in 1939 by a German theoretical astronomer, Rupert Wildt. Wildt put forward the hypothesis that the Red Spot is due to the presence of a large solid body, whose length and breadth are comparable with those of the Spot as we see it and whose depth is roughly the same as its breadth. This object he imagines to be floating, not in a liquid, but in an ocean of highly compressed permanent gases.

Peek considers first the well-known experiment of immersing an egg in a solution of salt and water. The solution is likely to be more concentrated toward the bottom and decrease in density upward. If an egg is put in the salt solution it will float at some level depending upon the density. Replace the salt solution by

Jupiter's atmosphere, in which the density increases rapidly with depth until it probably approaches the liquid state at only a moderate level. Let the egg be represented by some solid whose upper surface lies several score miles below the top of the cloud layer. Any disturbance which changes the density of the atmosphere will bring about a change in the level at which the solid will float. When a body sinks in the atmosphere it will rotate more rapidly, and when it rises, more slowly. This action is analogous to that of a skater whirling on ice. When the skater extends his arms he spins more slowly. When he wraps his arms tightly around himself he spins more rapidly. Peek shows that a range in depth of only about 6 miles would be sufficient to account for all the changes in the rotation period of the Red Spot that have been observed since 1831.

This still leaves the question of what it is that floats. Since the main constituents of Jupiter's atmosphere are the two lightest elements—hydrogen and helium—it must be some extremely light substance. The most promising material from which to construct a floating solid would appear to be helium. But a difficulty remains: at fairly low pressures, helium is the last of the elements to solidify, so that it is hard to find a remaining fluid in which such a solid can float. At present we simply do not have sufficient information about the Red Spot to form any idea of its nature.

▶ *How many moons does Jupiter have?*

Jupiter has twelve moons, but we should be careful to add that these are only the *known* moons. There are probably a good many more that have not been discovered. It is almost certain that if an experienced observer had a large telescope at his disposal and nothing to do with it but search for moons of Jupiter he would be almost sure to find some "new" ones. But the search is long and tedious and since Jupiter is known to have so many moons already it does not seem of great importance to tie up a large telescope on such a project.

The four large satellites of Jupiter were the first objects discovered with the telescope. They are often called the Galilean satellites, since their discovery is commonly credited to Galileo. (There is evidence that Galileo was preceded by a comparatively

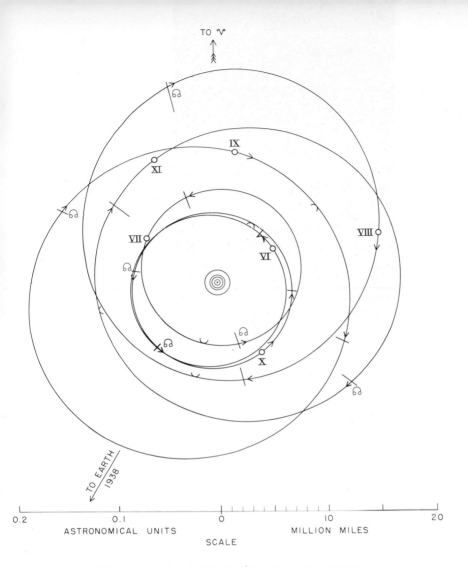

TO ♈

IX
XI
VIII
VII
VI
X

TO EARTH
1938

0.2   0.1   0   10   20

ASTRONOMICAL UNITS   MILLION MILES

SCALE

ORBITS OF JUPITER'S SATELLITES

63. Orbits of the moons of Jupiter. The four small orbits at
center are those of moons discovered by Galileo.

64. Successive photos of the four large moons of Jupiter showing motion.

unknown astronomer named Simon Mayer, who had been able to obtain a telescope in the summer of 1609 from the Netherlands. The subject has been investigated by the British Astronomical Association, which finds the evidence indicates that Mayer was an honest man and that his claims were not exaggerated. It appears to be the usual case of people assuming that a better-known man would naturally be first in everything, something that is not necessarily true.)

At any rate, these two observers saw the satellites as they appear today in a small telescope, bright points of light in a line on either side of Jupiter, perhaps two on one side and two on the other, or three or four on one side and one or none on the other. The satellites move so fast that their configuration will change appreciably in the course of a few hours' watching. This is particularly true of the first satellite, named Io, which revolves around the planet in only 42 hours. The satellites are so bright they could be seen by the unaided eye were they not so close to Jupiter as to be blotted out by the planet's glare. Seen in a large telescope, under good atmospheric conditions so that the images look crisp and sharp, these satellites do not appear as points of light, but show distinct disks. From observations of faint markings on the satellites as well as photometric measures of their brightness, it appears that they all revolve as our moon does in relation to the earth—they always keep the same side turned toward the planet.

A most interesting sight is that of the satellites in transit across the disk of the planet, as is that of the shadow of a satellite moving across the planet's disk. The black shadows are much easier to follow across the disk than the satellites themselves, since the satellites are of roughly the same brightness as the surface of Jupiter.

▶ *How were the satellites of Jupiter used in measuring the velocity of light?*

The first attempt to measure the velocity of light seems to have been made by Galileo, who had two observers signal back and forth by covering and uncovering the shutter on a lantern. Of course we know that the velocity of light is so great that no time lag could possibly have been detected by such crude methods. It was not until about fifty years later (in 1675) that the first scientific determination of the velocity of light was made.

A young Danish astronomer named Olaus Roemer had come to the Paris Observatory at the invitation of the director. Roemer made observations of the eclipses of Jupiter's satellites, especially Satellite I or Io. After watching the satellite go into eclipse behind Jupiter he worked out tables by which the time of the eclipse could be accurately predicted. The chief trouble was that the eclipses did not agree with the timetable but gradually got out of step with it. Roemer noticed that when the earth was moving away from Jupiter, so that the distance between the two planets was increas-

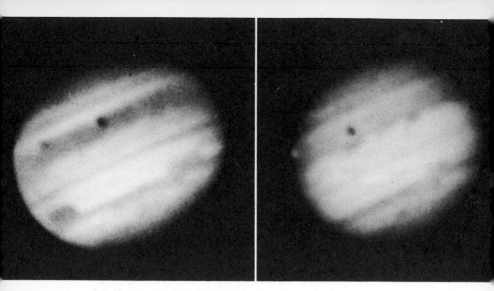

65. Photographs in infrared and ultraviolet light showing satellite and shadow on Jupiter.

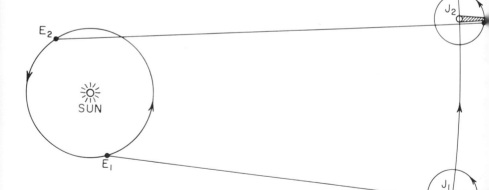

66. Roemer noticed that when the earth was approaching Jupiter the eclipses came earlier than when the earth was receding. He correctly interpreted this as due to the finite velocity of light across the earth's orbit.

ing, the eclipses kept coming later than the predicted time, whereas when the earth was approaching Jupiter the eclipses occurred earlier than predicted. Roemer correctly interpreted this as being due to the fact that the light by which we see the eclipses takes a definite time to travel across the earth's orbit. That is, as the distance is increasing the arrival of the light is delayed by the extra distance it has to travel, whereas when the two planets are approaching the distance is continually decreasing; we are moving forward to meet the light and the eclipse, so to speak, arrives earlier.

From his observations Roemer deduced that the time required for light to cross the 186 million miles of the earth's orbit was 20 minutes, which gives for the velocity of light a value of 156,000 miles per second. It is hard to time the eclipses accurately even today with modern instruments owing to the difficulty of telling precisely when the satellite moves into Jupiter's shadow; it was considerably more difficult with the crude instruments of former days, so that Roemer's value is remarkably good. Most of us find it hard to keep abreast of our times but Roemer was a man who was distinctly ahead of his. The idea of light traveling with some definite velocity through space seemed so farfetched that it was not accepted until fifty years later, when its velocity was measured by quite a different method.

▶ What kind of world is Saturn?

Saturn is a world similar to Jupiter except that we do not see the wealth of detailed cloud markings that are visible on the Jovian surface. Saturn is also perpetually covered by clouds which have never parted to reveal the surface below; these clouds are arranged in the form of belts of different shades crossing the disk, but the belts of Saturn encircle the planet in a smooth regular pattern instead of being irregular and turbulent along the edges as those of Jupiter are. Only very rarely have any markings appeared on the disk of Saturn from which the rotation period could be obtained. In 1876 Asaph Hall, discoverer of the satellites of Mars, observed a white spot near the equator that remained visible for several weeks, and which gave a rotation period of 10 hours 14 minutes 24 seconds. In 1903 a white spot appeared in latitude

147

67. Saturn and its rings. The rings are composed of small particles, each revolving around the planet in orbits of its own.

36 N. which gave a rotation period of 10 hours 38 minutes. In 1933 a white spot broke out suddenly near the equator which showed a rotation period of about the same value as that found by Hall. In 1939 the spectroscopic method of determining rotation was applied to Saturn by J. H. Moore at the Lick Observatory. He found a rotation period of 10 hours 2 minutes at the equator, increasing to 11 hours 8 minutes in latitude 57°.

Saturn is one of the most impressive objects visible in the telescope, chiefly due to its magnificent ring system. For some reason Saturn does not seem to be as much affected by bad seeing as other objects. I looked at Mars and Saturn one evening through a 6-inch refractor when the two planets were close together in the sky. Atmospheric disturbances made a mess out of Mars, while Saturn with its rings stood out clear and sharp.

The atmosphere of **Saturn**, like that of Jupiter, probably consists mainly of hydrogen and helium gas which cannot be detected

148

directly with the spectroscope. Methane and ammonia are the only gases for which we have direct observational evidence. The ammonia is not so abundant as in the atmosphere of Jupiter, probably because of the lower temperature. The clouds of Saturn may consist of ammonia cirrus.

The rings of Saturn are estimated to be only ten miles thick, so thin that when we see them edge-on they disappear even in the largest telescope. But they are of vast extent, measuring 41,500 miles in width with the distance of the innermost edge of the crepe ring (the one closest to Saturn) at a distance of 7000 miles from the planet's surface.

The rings look solid enough, but careful observation shows the edge of Saturn can be clearly seen through the crepe ring. Observations with the spectroscope show actually that the rings must be composed of tiny particles or meteorites, probably coated with frost or ice, each one revolving in a separate orbit of its own. That is, they consist of a mass of individual particles arranged around Saturn in the form of a ring—a satellite that was spoiled in the making.

▶ *What are the prospects of finding satellites of Mercury, Venus, and Pluto?*

Obviously prospects are not very good or satellites would have been discovered already. Yet perhaps they are not quite so dim as might appear at first glance. For one thing, nobody is making a determined effort to find a satellite of these bodies; the planets are neglected bodies in space. But the discovery by G. P. Kuiper in 1948 of a close satellite of Uranus and of a distant satellite of Neptune in 1949, besides the discovery since 1914 of four faint satellites of Jupiter by Seth B. Nicholson, gives some hope that the planets possess companions as yet unknown to us.

It would be particularly desirable to find satellites for Mercury, Venus, and Pluto, since the mass of these bodies is still very uncertain, but if satellites could be observed revolving around them their mass could be calculated quickly. At present the masses of these bodies can be found only by their disturbing effects on other bodies, and since the masses are small and the distances large, the disturbing effects are correspondingly small. Only recently has a reliable value for the mass of Mercury been determined by this method. (Apparently the first estimate of the mass of Mercury was obtained from the gravitational attraction of the planet upon Encke's comet when it made a close approach in 1842.) Something seems to be drastically wrong with our estimates of the size and mass of Pluto. From small irregularities in the motion of Uranus and Neptune a mass for Pluto has been obtained, about equal to that of the earth. From measures with the 200-inch telescope in 1948, a diameter of 3680 miles was found for Pluto. But if these values are correct, Pluto has a density ten times that of the earth or fifty-five times that of water. It seems incredible that Pluto can have so high a density. Estimates of its mass may be too big or those of its diameter too small, or maybe both are in error. And, while the mass of Venus is much more accurately determined than that of Mercury or Pluto, there is still room for improvement.

Let us consider first the possibility of discovering a satellite of Pluto. This is, of course, a project for a large telescope, for Pluto itself is so faint that a telescope of at least 17 inches aperture is required to see it. Suppose that Pluto has a satellite that reflects light, like our moon. Then at the average distance of Pluto, the size of a satellite corresponding to different visual magnitudes is shown in this table. It can be seen that, even assuming Pluto has a very large satellite, it would still be quite faint. The faintest star visible to the unaided eye is of the sixth magnitude, while Pluto itself is of the fourteenth magnitude. Magnitude 21 is about at the limit of the 100-inch telescope on Mount Wilson.

Satellite of Pluto

Visual magnitude	Diameter (miles)
17	1600
18	1000
19	630
20	400
21	250

If the diameter of Pluto is about 3680 miles and its satellite presumably much smaller, it seems unlikely that it can be much brighter than twentieth magnitude. Thus to be detected by present optical equipment it would have to be at least 200 miles in diam-

150

eter. Also, it would have to be revolving at a considerable distance from Pluto, say 100,000 miles, for its image to be separated from that of Pluto on the photographic plate. If the satellite were very large, say 1000 miles in diameter, it would undoubtedly have been detected by this time from the disturbing effect its gravitational attraction would produce on Pluto. The planet, instead of moving in a straight line, would move in a slightly wavy path which should be revealed from observations of the position of the planet. Since no such wavy motion for Pluto has been reported it is presumed that the planet cannot have a satellite of any size attracting it.

The best time to search for a satellite of Venus would be when the planet is at maximum brightness, which occurs about 36 days from the time when Venus is directly in front of the sun, or at *inferior conjunction,* as astronomers say. At this time Venus shows a crescent phase like that of the moon about five days old and the satellite would show the same phase as the planet. Assuming again that the satellite reflects light as the surface of our moon does, we can take different magnitudes for the satellite and calculate the size corresponding to them. Here are the diameters for a hypothetical satellite of Venus:

Satellite of Venus

Visual magnitude	Diameter (miles)
10	44
12	17
14	7
16	3
18	1

The two little satellites of Mars, Phobos and Deimos, are of about magnitude 12.6 and are estimated to be 7 and 5 miles in diameter respectively. The fifth satellite of Jupiter is magnitude 13 and its computed diameter is 150 miles. So from the table for Venus it seems unlikely that Venus can have an undiscovered companion more than 50 miles in diameter.

The satellite would be easiest to spot when it is at *elongation;* that is, when it appears to be at its greatest distance from the planet. Suppose the search is confined to ten days before the date

151

of maximum brightness. At this time Venus is about 45° from the sun. The observer will be lucky if he has an hour when he can work to advantage. Unless the satellite just *happens* to be near elongation during this hour he may never see it.

Search for a satellite of Venus would be further complicated by the great brightness of this planet and the fact that the exposure would have to be taken in a twilight sky. Perhaps a return to the old visual methods might prove more effective. Three of the most elusive satellites in the solar system were discovered in this way— Phobos, Deimos, and Jupiter V.

8 ▶ ASTEROIDS AND THEIR DISCOVERY

▶ *What is Bode's law?*

Bode's law is a complete misnomer. It is not a law and it was not discovered by Bode. It is nothing more than an interesting little numerical trick for remembering the distance of the planets from the sun. Just who should have the credit for first formulating it is uncertain, but it seems to have originated with J. D. Titius, a professor in the University of Wittenberg, who published it in a translation of a scientific work in 1772. It was given wide publicity by J. E. Bode, who was editor of the influential *Astronomisches Jahrbuch,* so that it is generally associated with his name.

This numerical relationship goes as follows:

List the planets in the order of their distance from the sun. Write a 4 below each planet. To the first 4 add 0; to the second add 3; to the third add 6; to the next 12, and so on. Then divide these numbers by 10. The resulting figures give the distance of the planets from the sun in terms of the earth's distance as 1.0.

	Mercury	Venus	Earth	Mars	?	Jupiter	Saturn	Uranus	Neptune	Pluto
	4	4	4	4	4	4	4	4	4	4
Bode's	0	3	6	12	24	48	96	192	384	768
law	0.4	0.7	1.0	1.6	2.8	5.2	10.0	19.6	38.8	77.7
True distance	0.4	0.7	1.0	1.5	?	5.2	9.5	19.2	30.1	39.5

▶ *How was the first asteroid discovered?*

It is seen that "Bode's law" breaks down badly in the case of Neptune and fails completely for Pluto. Of course, in Bode's time, the planets only out as far as Uranus were known and when

153

distance for them was found to agree so closely with the law, confidence in it was greatly strengthened. The only thing wrong was the glaring gap at 2.8 astronomical units from the sun. Bode believed there simply *must* be a planet at this distance if only it could be discovered, and his writing and lectures on the subject did much to influence public opinion in behalf of finding it. As a result, a sort of astronomical police force of twenty-four astronomers was organized for the purpose of making a systematic search for a small body, by dividing up the zodiac among them, and giving a portion to each member. But before they ever had a chance to go into action, word came of the discovery of the kind of body for which they were seeking by an astronomer who was not even a member of the group. On the evening of January 1, 1801, Giuseppe Piazzi, a professor of astronomy and mathematics at Palermo, Sicily, accidentally found an object in the constellation of Taurus which moved from night to night and which was therefore not a star.

Piazzi had followed the new planet for six weeks when he became ill and was unable to continue. Soon the sun by its eastward motion had come so near the asteroid that it vanished. When the time came for the asteroid to reappear the question was where to look for it. Trying to find it a second time was almost as difficult as trying to find it in the first place. So far as appearances go, the little body was indistinguishable from the stars around it. And there are so many stars that trying to spot a particular one that is moving is an exceedingly difficult proposition. You can't imagine how difficult it is unless, in fact, you try it. Then you are likely to feel so dismayed you will want to give up immediately. It takes a person with extraordinary patience and capacity for minute detail to make a success of such a job.

Today the problem would seem almost too easy. With as much as six weeks of observation it would be a routine matter to compute an orbit for the body which should pinpoint it so closely there would be no trouble whatever in picking it up at its new position. This would be especially easy since photography instead of visual search could be applied to the problem. But in those days there was not even any straightforward method for computing the orbit or path of a newly discovered body. Fortunately, the great mathematician Karl Friedrich Gauss had recently perfected a method

154

for determining the orbit of a newly discovered object from only three observations of its position, although in actual practice a good many more are needed to define the orbit with any precision. Today two general methods of calculating the orbit of a planet or comet are available: the one by Gauss just mentioned and another, with a different method of approach, originated by Pierre Simon Laplace. Which one is better is largely a matter of personal opinion. Both should of course give the same result for the same object.

Using Piazzi's observations of the previous winter, Gauss used his method to calculate where the planet should be, and it was found without difficulty before the end of the year. Piazzi named it Ceres, after the Roman goddess of agriculture. Gauss' calculations showed the distance of Ceres from the sun was 2.8 astronomical units, in exact agreement with Bode's law!

▶ *What are the asteroids?*

The object that Piazzi discovered was a little body known as an asteroid or minor planet. As it happened, Piazzi discovered the largest of the asteroids—the diameter of Ceres is 480 miles. Although Ceres is the largest asteroid, it is not the brightest; that honor goes to one named Vesta, which is only 240 miles in diameter but is the only asteroid visible to the unaided eye. After Ceres was discovered in 1801, the second asteroid, Pallas, was discovered a year later during the course of the search for Ceres. Juno was discovered in 1804 and Vesta in 1807. Then followed a long gap during which no asteroid was discovered until 1845, when one was finally turned up by an amateur astronomer named Hencke after fifteen years of fruitless search. This fifth asteroid Hencke named Astraea. Search in the early nineteenth century was very laborious. It was necessary to make special maps of the stars in a region of the sky along which the sun moves and where asteroids are most likely to be found. Then these maps were compared with the stars from time to time to see if an object could be seen in the sky which did not appear on the charts.

By this method, if an object is sighted which does not appear on the charts it is under suspicion at once as a possible asteroid. Its position in relation to the stars close around it is carefully noted

155

and then followed for a while to see if it is moving. Usually a few hours' watch will show whether the object is moving or not, or its position can be checked again the following night. The method sounds easy in principle but is very difficult to apply in practice. There are so many ways you can make a mistake. There may be an error in the positions of the stars on your star map. Many stars vary in brightness. A new suspicious object may be merely a variable star that was too faint to be noticed when the map was made, but which has increased in brightness since. Also, looking back and forth continually between map and telescope is a tedious and laborious operation. How Hencke ever managed to keep up such a search for fifteen years defies imagination. What a world of patience the man must have had, working over his bread and pastry during the day, and peering through his little telescope until the late hours of the night. One cannot help wondering what Frau Hencke thought of her husband's project. Or was he a bachelor? At any rate, Hencke discovered another asteroid in 1847, which he named Hebe.

▶ How are asteroids discovered today?

Discovering an asteroid today is almost too easy. In fact, it is often hard *not* to discover an asteroid. Anyone who has access to a good-sized photographic telescope and who wants to take the trouble can easily find one. The main difficulty now is making sure you have discovered a new one and not one of the sixteen hundred or more that have already been discovered and named. Today most asteroids are picked up accidentally while an astronomer is taking an exposure on some region of the sky for another purpose. Remember that the asteroid is *moving* against the background of *fixed* stars. Now the telescope is attached to a driving mechanism that turns it across the sky at the same rate as that of the stars. Hence the stars appear on the photographic plate as small round dots even though the exposure may be an hour long, since the telescope is made to track with the stars. But the asteroid will *not* be moving at the same rate as the stars, so that instead of appearing on the plate as a *dot,* it will appear drawn out into a *streak,* the length of the streak depending upon the length of the exposure and how fast the asteroid is moving. The streak left by the asteroid can usually be distinguished quite readily from the round star images.

There is another photographic method that is even more effective in ferreting out faint asteroids. It is easy to see that the image of an asteroid formed on the photographic plate will be more intense if it is all concentrated at one point instead of being drawn out into a streak. This may be done by giving the plateholder a slow motion during the exposure, equal to that of the motion of the average asteroid in the region of the sky under observation. In this method the photographs show the stars as streaks while an asteroid will appear as nearly a round spot, but much stronger than if the image had been allowed to trail in the usual way.

Today so many asteroids have been discovered that there is little point in looking for more. To show how easily asteroids may be discovered, Seth B. Nicholson of the Mount Wilson Observatory —searching for new satellites of Jupiter with the 100-inch telescope—picked up thirty-two asteroids on his plates, each one a decided nuisance since it had to be eliminated as a possible Jovian moon. Today an astronomer may often pick up an asteroid trail on one of his plates and not bother to do anything about it unless its motion is unusual in some way. By "unusual" is generally meant rapid motion indicating that the asteroid comes exceptionally close to the earth. Such asteroids give us more information about the nature of the solar system than we can obtain from dozens moving in the average way. Often trying to fix the orbit of such a body develops into an exciting game of hide and seek, with the asteroid as elusive as a fox trying to escape hunters.

▶ How was Icarus discovered?

The story of Icarus illustrates the merry chase that an asteroid sometimes leads astronomers before it is caught, never to escape again. Icarus was discovered accidentally by Dr. Walter Baade on June 26, 1949, while he was taking a photograph of the sky near the bright red star Antares with the 48-inch telescope on Palomar Mountain. The trail the asteroid left on the plate was so long it would have moved the apparent diameter of the moon in 11 hours. Two more photographs of the asteroid were obtained on June 28 and June 30. Not wishing to calculate the orbit of the

157

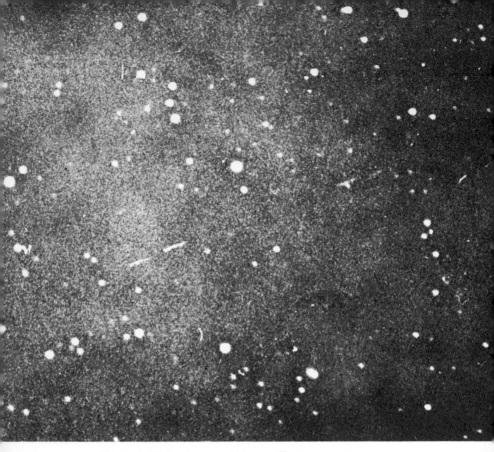

68. Trails left by the asteroid Icarus. The stars appear as round spots.

object himself, Dr. Baade turned his plates over to Dr. Seth B. Nicholson of the Mount Wilson and Palomar Observatories and myself, after which he left on his vacation, leaving us to toil over the computation of the orbit in the broiling hot days that followed. At that time I did not particularly relish the job, but as it turned out I would not have missed it for anything.

Our first rough calculations on the orbit indicated the object had a mean distance from the sun less than that of the earth (93 million miles). If true it would be the only object in the solar

158

system known to have, with the exception of Mercury and Venus. A real find! Our chief problem at the time was to keep it from getting lost. For our first orbit was only good enough to predict positions for about three weeks ahead, at the most. Unless we could obtain more observations with which to get a better orbit, this asteroid would surely be lost, just as other remarkable asteroids—Hermes and Apollo and Adonis—are hopelessly lost today.

Fortunately we were able to make observations on July 12 and 13 which gave us a fairly reliable orbit. Nobody knows how close Icarus came to being lost at this time, for it had reached what is called the "stationary" point in its path, where the combination of the earth's motion and the planet's motion makes it appear practically to stand still in the sky. As a result, the image of the asteroid on the plates appeared almost a round dot, the same as the star images. How Nicholson managed to pick it out from the hundreds of star images on the plates I shall never know. Rather to our chagrin the computations based on our new positions of the asteroid showed that its mean distance from the sun was slightly greater than the earth's mean distance from the sun. The object had an orbit that, instead of being round like that of a planet, was elongated like that of a comet. It comes within 21 million miles of the sun at closest approach—well inside the orbit of Mercury, the planet closest to the sun. Farthest from the sun it recedes beyond the orbit of Mars to a distance of 177 million miles.

Dr. Baade chose Icarus as the most appropriate name for the asteroid. In classic mythology, Icarus was the son of Daedalus, who seems to have been the first aeronaut. The pair escaped from prison by attaching wings to their bodies with wax and flying over the Aegean Sea. Icarus, refusing to heed his father's advice, flew too near the sun so that his wings melted, and he plunged into the sea. Let us hope in the future that the orbit of Icarus is never so disturbed by the other planets that the asteroid meets a similar fate.

It is of interest to gain some notion of the range in temperature that this body undergoes in its trip around the sun. At its closest approach to the sun, the highest temperature of a nonrotating airless black planet would be about 1000° F. The temperature at which a body becomes hot enough to glow so that it can be seen is about 800° F. So it is possible that when nearest the sun the surface of this asteroid becomes hot enough to glow a dull red. But the temperature may be considerably below this figure if the asteroid is rotating rapidly and its surface is gray instead of black. Six months later, when the planet is farthest from the sun the temperature of the surface must be far below freezing.

The great importance of Icarus to science is that it furnishes us a body that is nearly ideal for testing the general theory of relativity. The theory of relativity predicts that the point on the orbit of a planet nearest the sun should shift around toward the east by a calculable amount. Before Icarus came along, Mercury was the best object for making such a test. But Icarus has a much higher "figure of merit" for making this test than Mercury. The only trouble is that Icarus will have to be observed for about a century before we can tell whether or not it is moving as predicted.

▶ *Where did the asteroids come from?*

The origin of the asteroids is unknown. One theory is that they represent fragmentary material circulating between the orbits of Mars and Jupiter which for some reason never coalesced to form a planet.

Another theory is that they originated from an exploding planet. If a planet did explode, the fragments, of course, would originate at the point of explosion, and as the fragments moved off in their various orbits they would all have to return and pass again through the point where the catastrophe occurred. If there were nothing to disturb the motion of the fragments, it should be possible to locate this point in space years later. But the disturbing action due to the gravitational attraction of Jupiter has changed the orbits to such an extent that all trace of their point of origin is now completely lost. Some support to this idea is given by the work of Hirayama, who has shown that many of the asteroids may be grouped into "families," the members of the same family having the same orbital characteristics as if they had a common origin. This would indicate that there was not one explosion but rather a series of explosions that formed the different asteroid families. The trouble is, it is so hard to think of any reason why a planet should

160

explode in the first place. (The total mass of the asteroids is estimated to be only about 4/10,000 that of the earth.)

A more likely suggestion is that the asteroids were created by a collision between larger parent masses in the asteroid zone. The six asteroid families discovered by Hirayama may be regarded as due to relatively recent secondary collisions. From this point of view the "catastrophe" in the asteroid ring was not a single event but a never-ending process which is still going on and which will continue to produce both other asteroids and meteorites in the future.

9 ▶ BODIES BETWEEN THE PLANETS

▶ *What is a comet?*

A comet has been called a "great big bag full of nothing." This is an exaggeration, of course, but there is a certain element of truth in it. A comet occupies a tremendous volume of space. It is always larger than the earth and may be as large as the sun. But it has very little matter in it. Its mass is small. Most of a comet consists of empty space with a little gas and dust distributed through it. This gas and dust is rendered visible by the light of the sun. The comet gives off no light of its own. Thus most comets are invisible when they are as far away as Jupiter and only begin to brighten up as they approach closer to the sun.

Comets used to be regarded as omens of evil, foretelling wars, pestilence, famine, and the death of kings. And since there is nearly always something bad going on in history it was never hard for superstitious people to claim that these predictions were fulfilled. During the Middle Ages there seemed to be no limit to the imagination in describing the appearance of comets. Writers of the time saw in them swords of fire, bleeding crosses, flaming daggers, spears, dragons, and other objects of horror. Even some of the most serious writers let their imaginations run completely riot when they came to describing comets. Thus a noted surgeon, Ambrose Pare, described a comet that appeared in 1528 in the following terms: "This comet was so horrible and frightful, and produced such great terror among the populace, that some died of fear; others fell sick. It appeared as a star of excessive length and of the color of blood; at its summit was seen the figure of a *bent arm* holding a great sword in its hand, *as if about to strike*. At this point there were three stars. On both sides of the rays of this comet

162

were seen a great number of axes, knives, spaces colored with blood, among which were a great number of hideous human faces with beards and bristling hair!" We should not consider people of another day completely crazy in this regard, however. Even in modern times comets have inspired fear among the population. Thus when Halley's comet appeared in 1910 there were people who did a brisk business selling "comet pills" to the ignorant to protect them against the malign influence of the hairy star.

▶ How was Halley's comet discovered?

We owe Edmund Halley (1656–1742) a great debt for ridding us of some of our superstitious notions about comets.

69. Views of Halley's comet at its most recent appearance, in 1910.

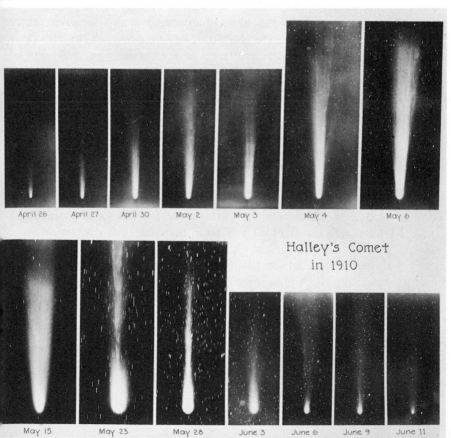

| April 26 | April 27 | April 30 | May 2 | May 3 | May 4 | May 6 |

Halley's Comet
in 1910

| May 15 | May 23 | May 28 | June 3 | June 6 | June 9 | June 11 |

Comets seem to move in a wildly erratic manner quite different from the slow, orderly motion of the planets. They appear suddenly in any part of the sky, remain visible for a few weeks, and then depart, usually never to be seen again. As late as the sixteenth century they were not even supposed to belong to the region of the planets but to exist in the earth's upper atmosphere. Halley did much to dispel these ideas by being the first to predict the return of a comet. He based his prediction upon the fact that the orbit of a comet in 1682 was nearly identical with those of comets that had appeared in 1607 and 1531, and he suspected they were not three different comets, but returns of the same comet at intervals of seventy-five and seventy-six years. He also found records of the appearance of a bright comet at similar intervals in the years 1456, 1301, 1145, and 1066. He noted that the intervals between were not equal, and attributed it to the disturbing action of Jupiter and Saturn upon the motion of the comet. In 1705 Halley published a *Synopsis of Cometary Astronomy* in which he predicted that the comet would return sometime early in the year 1759, mathematics not having advanced sufficiently at that time to predict its return more accurately. The prediction of the return of a comet was an unheard-of thing in those days, and many scientific men scoffed at Halley's bold prediction, pointing out that as he could hardly hope to attain the age of 102, he would not be on hand to see if it were fulfilled or not. As the time of the predicted return drew near, speculation over the comet's appearance mounted rapidly.

The great mathematical astronomer, Clairaut, set himself the task of fixing the time of perihelion passage, when the comet came nearest the sun, with the greatest precision possible. This necessitated long calculations in order to keep track of the disturbing influence of the giant planets upon the comet for every step of its journey since 1607. Clairaut hoped to be able to announce the time of perihelion passage before the comet was even sighted if it should return. A close agreement between theory and observation would then come as a triumph for the principles of gravitational astronomy.

We can easily imagine how intently the computers toiled over their rows of figures, driven by the thought of the comet rushing nearer and nearer at an ever-increasing pace. There is a certain

164

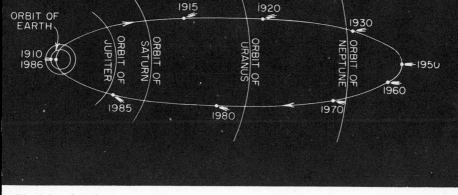

70. Orbit of Halley's comet, showing positions from 1910 to its next return in 1986.

hypnotic fascination about numerical computation that is hard to understand unless one has experienced it. The desire to obtain an orbit that will fit the motion of an object in space can become so absorbing as to banish everything else from mind. "During six months we calculated from morning till night, sometimes even at meals," wrote one member of the computing staff, "the consequence of which was that I contracted an illness which changed my constitution during the remainder of my life."

As a result of these calculations Clairaut was able to announce to the Academy of Sciences on November 14, 1758, that the comet would pass perihelion on April 13, 1759. It was first sighted by an amateur astronomer on Christmas day of 1758, and passed perihelion 32 days before the time set by Clairaut, very good agreement considering the numerous uncertainties involved.

▶ *How are comets discovered?*

Because comets are occasionally spectacular objects whose brief appearance in the sky arouses widespread notice, there has always been considerable popular interest in their discovery. The discovery of a comet is not at all a rare event, with perhaps a dozen or so discovered every year. Most of these are faint objects which never become visible to the naked eye, or are so faintly

165

visible as to attract little attention. Until recently, however, the Astronomical Society of the Pacific awarded a medal for the discovery of an unexpected comet, and back in the last century one philanthropic individual offered a cash prize for the discovery of a comet. It is said that the astronomer Edward Emerson Barnard paid for his home from money derived in this way. Every time the mortgage came due he was able to discover a comet to meet the payment.

Some individuals make a business of searching for comets systematically. They employ a telescope called a "comet seeker," one which has a fairly large lens of short focal length, giving a wide bright field of view. Comets come in toward the sun from all directions, but probably the best place to "sweep" for comets is in the opposite direction from the sun or *in opposition,* as astronomers say. Upon sighting a comet the news is telegraphed to the Harvard College Observatory, which acts as a clearing house for newly discovered objects of all kinds. There is a regular code for sending such a message, which gives information on the position of the comet, its direction of motion, general appearance, and whether it has a tail or not. Upon receiving such information the news is then telegraphed to leading observatories over the United States. Often several people will discover a comet almost at the same time and it is hard to decide who has priority. Thus a comet may bear the name of several people, as for example Comet Bappu–Bok–Newkirk.

▶ *When do comets become visible?*

Comets seldom become visible when they are more than about five times the distance of the earth from the sun, which puts them out around the orbit of Jupiter. When first sighted at great distances they usually appear simply as a round hazy patch of light or *coma* surrounding one or more bright starlike points of light in the nucleus. The tail is missing and does not begin to develop until the comet nears the sun. It is generally considered that the mass of a comet is concentrated in its nucleus and that the coma and tail originate from gas and dust generated in the nucleus. The nucleus is supposed to consist of a conglomeration of meteorites of all sizes, ranging from tiny particles microscopic

166

71. Finsler's comet on August 9, 1937. The telescope was
made to move with the comet so that the stars are drawn out
into streaks.

in size up to blocks several miles in diameter. As the comet approaches the sun the nucleus becomes heated so that the gas escapes from the surface layers. It is material derived from the nucleus that forms the head and tail of the comet. Since material is continually leaving the nucleus, never to return, it is clear that a comet is steadily losing material without ever having any chance of regaining it. Thus in the natural order of events a comet must continually grow smaller and in the end finally be dissipated completely.

The tail of a comet always streams from the head in a direction away from the sun. This looks as if there must be some repulsive force from the sun acting on the cometary material causing it to stream away in this manner. The material in the head does not always appear to be smoothly streaming away from it. Often jets issue toward the sun from the nucleus, then spread out into a fan-shaped mass which sweeps outward and backward into the tail. Disruptive forces appear to be at work within a comet, so violent that they have been known to cause a comet to split into two, moving along side by side through space. The motions observed are larger than would be expected from the action of light pressure alone, so that it has been suggested that much of the more violent motion observed in comets may be due to corpuscular radiation emanating from the sun. The continuous flow of particles from the sun exerts sufficient pressure on the matter in comets' tails to produce the large motions observed, indicating that forces stronger than that of light pressure are at work.

Fred L. Whipple of the Harvard College Observatory has proposed an ingenious explanation to account for some of the motions (such as jets) observed in the heads of comets. Whipple's comet model has a nucleus composed of a conglomerate of ices and solids. Some of the outer layers of ice would evaporate, leaving a porous crust of meteoritic material which covers up the rest of the nucleus and acts as an insulating layer. As the comet approaches the sun the temperature of the nucleus rises and the hot gases present tend to disrupt the meteoritic crust, thus exposing part of the icy interior to the intense radiation of the sun. As a result of the rapid vaporization in these exposed regions, the gases rush out in the form of jets. When a stream of gas leaves the cometary nucleus it has a jet-propulsion effect on the comet itself. In other words,

168

the comet will undergo a change in motion as it moves along its orbit due to the repulsive action of the jet. Such effects would change the period of the comet; hence it might arrive ahead of or behind its schedule, depending upon how the jet acted. In this way the steady change in the period of Encke's comet is explained as due to the expulsion of gases from the nucleus, always different from the direction of the sun.

▶ *How do comets move?*

The planets and all except a few remarkable asteroids move in nearly circular orbits. There are a very few comets that also move in nearly circular orbits. But most comets move in very elongated orbits called *ellipses*. (An ellipse is a closed type of curve.) A body moving in an ellipse will always eventually return to the original point from which it started. There is another type of curve in which a comet might travel, called a *hyperbola*. (A hyperbola is an open curve having two branches stretching out to an immeasurably great distance in each direction.) A body moving in a hyperbola will approach the sun along one branch of the curve, swing past it, and then go on out into space along the other branch—never to return. Because we can observe a comet only over a very small part of its path when it is close to the sun, it is often hard to tell whether it is moving in a hyperbola or a tremendously elongated ellipse. But from a list of twenty accurately calculated orbits of comets moving outside the solar system none were found to be hyperbolic. All were elliptical. But what immense ellipses! They stretch almost to the stars. Their periods, of course, are correspondingly long. Nearly 80 per cent of the comets we observe have periods greater than a hundred years and the longest have periods of millions of years. The major axes of the orbits of these comets are measured in thousands of astronomical units, abbreviated A.U. (An astronomical unit is equal to the distance of the earth from the sun, 93 million miles.) When we consider that the distance of the nearest star is 270,000 A.U. we realize that the comets in the course of their wandering, at their greatest distance from the sun, reach regions where their paths could be affected by the gravitational attraction of the nearest stars.

169

▶ What is Jupiter's "family of comets"?

There are other comets with periods of only a few years whose orbits extend out only to about the distance of Jupiter. That so many comets have orbits extending to about this particular distance can hardly be the result of chance. It is probable that these comets once passed very close to Jupiter, possibly moving in very elongated orbits, and had their paths radically changed by the planet's gravitational attraction so that thenceforth they moved in orbits of an entirely different type. If the gravitational attraction of Jupiter speeds up the comet it will go off into space in a hyperbolic orbit. If it is slowed down it may move in an elliptical orbit of short period, and the comet will return at regular intervals, moving in a path which passes through the point where the disturbance took place. It can be shown that the orbit of a comet might be transformed by a single encounter with Jupiter from a very elongated orbit into an ellipse with a period as short as five years if the comet passed within 200,000 miles of Jupiter.

▶ What is a cometary anti-tail?

Occasionally a comet has been sighted which had a long spike or *anti-tail* projecting from its head in a sunward direction. At first glance this seems to contradict the statement that the tail of a comet always points in a direction away from the sun. One of the most interesting comets of recent times to display an anti-tail was Arend–Roland (1956h), discovered as a faint telescopic object on November 6, 1956. By the following April it had become visible to the naked eye and attracted wide attention. About two weeks after passing perihelion it suddenly developed a long sunward spike which grew until it had a length of two million miles. (Fig. 72.) Then just as suddenly it disappeared. The appearance of the anti-tail was entirely an effect of perspective, and does not in any way constitute an anomaly in cometary behavior.

We can readily explain the effect if we assume that Comet Arend–Roland was enveloped in a thin layer of debris lying very nearly in the plane of its orbit. When viewed broadside from the earth so that we are looking *through* the layer, it is so thin as to be invisible. It is like looking directly at an outstretched fan made of some fine, nearly transparent material. This is the way we viewed

170

72. Comet Arend-Roland showing anti-tail on April 26, 1957.
This was when earth was in plane of cometary debris, so that
we were looking through greatest thickness.

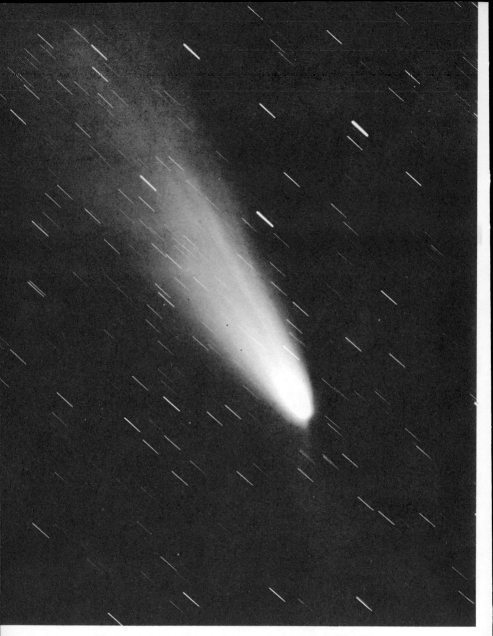

73. Comet Arend-Roland, photographed on April 29, 1957,
after earth had moved out of plane of cometary debris.

172

the comet the first time. But after the comet passed by the sun we viewed the layer nearly edge-on so that we were looking through its entire thickness. The result was that the layer illuminated by the sun appeared as a long, narrow bright line projected against the background of the sky. The effect only lasted a short time, while the earth was in the plane of the cometary debris.

▶ *What would happen if a comet were to hit the earth?*

This all depends upon the size of the bodies involved. We should certainly have a splendid shower of shooting stars produced by the myriads of smaller particles entering our atmosphere. The bombardment due to larger masses weighing thousands of tons could be much more serious and create widespread damage, although it would hardly wipe out life all over the earth since the dimensions of the nucleus of a comet are only about 1000 miles in diameter. It is probable that during geologic time the earth has been struck by many comets. As a matter of fact, we already know the effects produced by a small comet or large meteorite that struck in Siberia on June 30, 1908. The explosion resulting from the fall was recorded on seismographs all over the world. The column of fire raised by the fall was seen from a distance of 250 miles, and the crash and several thunderclaps produced were heard 600 miles from the point of contact. Trees were blown down from the center of the fall for scores of miles. According to L. A. Kulik of the Russian Academy of Sciences, who investigated this fall in 1927, as far away as 250 miles fences were overturned, people carrying grain sacks were knocked down, and as far as 400 miles distant workers on rafts were thrown into the river and horses could not stand on their feet! Fortunately this collision occurred in an uninhabited region so that no lives were lost. The effects of such a collision in a heavily populated region could be devastating, fully as bad or worse than the explosion of a hydrogen bomb. We must remember, however, that the probability of such a collision is exceedingly small. It can be shown that a small, rapidly moving body that approaches to within one astronomical unit stands about one chance in 400 million of hitting the earth. About five comets come within this distance every year, so on the average the nucleus of a comet should hit the earth about once every 80 million years.

173

When we also remember how much of the earth's surface is covered by water the probability of a serious collision with a comet is infinitesimal.

Thus we see that the chance of a head-on collision with the nucleus of a comet is practically nil. The chance that the earth might pass through the head or tail of a comet is considerably better owing to its vastly larger size. When Halley's comet was 180 million miles from the sun its head was 220,000 miles in diameter, or about 30 times that of the earth. The tail of a comet is enormous, streaming off from the head to distances of 30 to 50 million miles in the case of bright comets, and several cases are known in which the length of the tail was as great as 100 million miles, or about equal to the distance of the earth from the sun.

While there is little danger of collision, it has been suggested that some of the gases in the head and tail might poison the atmosphere. But the cometary gases are so thinly distributed that it is impossible for them to cause us any trouble. Moreover, combination of the gases in a comet's tail with the gases of our atmosphere would immediately render them harmless. The contamination from the smog of our large cities is undoubtedly much more harmful. It is probable that the earth actually passed through the tail of the great comet of 1861, and through the tail of Halley's comet on May 18, 1910. In neither case was anything unusual noted.

▶ *How did comets originate?*

Nobody knows how comets originated. There is only speculation on the subject.

One of the oldest hypotheses of the origin of comets is that they came from material expelled from Jupiter or the other giant planets with high velocity. For material to fly away from the surface of a planet never to return it would have to be expelled into space by an explosion having a velocity greater than the so-called "velocity of escape." The velocity of escape is 37 miles per second for Jupiter, 22 miles per second for Saturn, and about 14 miles per second for Uranus and Neptune. These are very high velocities and would require tremendous forces to send masses into space with such speeds. The hypothesis was originally suggested in 1870 by Richard A. Proctor in the days when Jupiter was considered to be

174

a semi-sun instead of a cold body as we think of it at present. From the point of view of velocity the earth or moon would seem to be a better source of cometary material, since the velocity of escape from the earth is 7 miles per second and only 1.5 miles per second for the moon. There is also the difficulty of getting the material through the atmosphere of a planet like Jupiter or even of the earth. At such high velocities the resistance of an atmosphere would be so great that it is difficult to see how much material could escape into space. The moon—which probably never had an atmosphere—would seem to be more effective in forming comets. This hypothesis implies that the comets were formed millions of years ago when volcanic activity was much more prevalent than at present. But within the solar system comets are subject to dissipation of their material by such corpuscular radiation from the sun that they are torn apart after comparatively short lives. On this basis it is hard to see how the comets could have survived so long intact.

Another hypothesis is that comets and asteroids were formed by the explosion of a planet revolving between the orbits of Mars and Jupiter. The cause of the explosion is left a mystery. Some of the fragments resulting from the explosion were supposed to have nearly circular orbits while others were elongated ellipses. Those having nearly circular orbits remained stable members of the solar system, while those in elliptical orbits were subjected to the disturbing gravitational attraction of Jupiter and other planets in such a way that they were diffused far out into space beyond the confines of the solar system. Most of these would be moving in hyperbolic orbits and so would leave the solar system, never to return, but a small portion would have been thrown into orbits with major axes in the neighborhood of 50,000 to 100,000 astronomical units. These would form a kind of cloud of comets at vast distances from the sun. From the number of comets that pass by our sun we can form an estimate of the total number in this cometary shell: close to a hundred million. Occasionally, as a result of the disturbing action of the nearer stars, a comet's orbit is changed so that it is, so to speak, admitted to the realm of the planets as a short-period comet, there to spend its remaining years dissipating its substance at each close approach to the sun.

175

▶ *What at present is the greatest anomaly in the theory of gravitation?*

Newton's law of gravitation has been so successful in predicting the motion of the heavenly bodies in the minutest detail that long ago it came to be accepted without question. On certain occasions when astronomers have felt that some slight change in this simple law was needed, later study has always revealed that something was wrong with their method of investigation. In a few cases, persistent differences between observation and gravitational theory have resulted in important discoveries of an unexpected kind. Thus a slight but definite change in the orientation of Mercury's orbit was finally explained by the general theory of relativity. More recently, apparent irregularities in the motion of the moon and planets have been traced to the fact that the earth itself does not rotate at a steady rate.

Probably the greatest anomaly in the theory of gravitation at present is in the so-called secular acceleration of Encke's comet. That is, on the average Encke's comet keeps moving around the sun a little faster all the time. Since this comet was first observed by an astronomer named Mechain, on January 17, 1786, its period of revolution has decreased from 1212.8 days to 1210.2 days in 1947, or at the average rate of 70 minutes per revolution. This may not seem like very much, but it is a great deal to the astronomers who make it their business to try to pin down the motion of comets in the sky. If the time it takes the comet to go around the sun is getting shorter all the time, the average speed of the body must be increasing or accelerating. The trouble is that the acceleration behaves in such an erratic manner that despite the enormous amount of work that has been done on this particular comet, it still refuses to move according to prediction.

▶ *How did Encke's comet get its name?*

As often happens in comet hunting, Encke's comet was "discovered" several times before its true identity was recognized. On November 26, 1818, Jean Louis Pons at Marseilles picked up a small telescopic comet which he followed for the next seven weeks. Johann Franz Encke went to work calculating the orbit of the comet and found that it was moving in an oval path

176

or ellipse with a period of 3.3 years. (It is still the shortest periodic comet on record.) Encke saw that the path of the comet agreed so closely in position with comets observed in 1786, 1795, and 1805 that he felt almost sure they must be different returns of the same body. But being almost sure is far from being certain, and Encke's curiosity was aroused to such an extent that he determined to settle the matter. This meant going through the tedious process of calculating the position of the comet backward, step by step, allowing for the disturbing effects of the planets whenever they became large enough to be sensible. Such calculations are still extremely laborious and the work must have been much more difficult in Encke's day, without the aid of special tables or mechanical computing machines. Yet within six weeks Encke had carried the computation through and established beyond doubt that the Pons comet of 1818 was identical with the three previously observed, and that it must have passed the point nearest the sun or perihelion seven times between 1786 and 1818 without being detected. He also predicted the time of the comet's next return in 1822 so accurately that forever afterward astronomers (with one exception) have called it Encke's, the single exception being Encke himself who always referred to it as Pons' comet. Encke must have been a furious worker, for somehow he managed to accomplish all this by his twenty-eighth year while he was still studying under Karl Friedrich Gauss at Göttingen, and in spite of active military service from 1811 to 1815 as a sergeant-major in the horse artillery.

▶ How was the "resisting medium" discovered?

As early as August, 1820, Encke suspected the speed of his comet was gradually increasing. After having eliminated the disturbing effects of the planets, the times of perihelion passage when the planet came nearest the sun from 1786 to 1819 showed that the period was getting smaller at the rate of about 0.11 days per revolution. When the comet at its next return in 1822 again showed a diminution of the same amount, Encke felt justified in supposing that some unknown force must be acting to produce it. In this way he was led to his famous hypothesis of a resisting medium which, by opposing the motion of the comet, had the effect of increasing its speed.

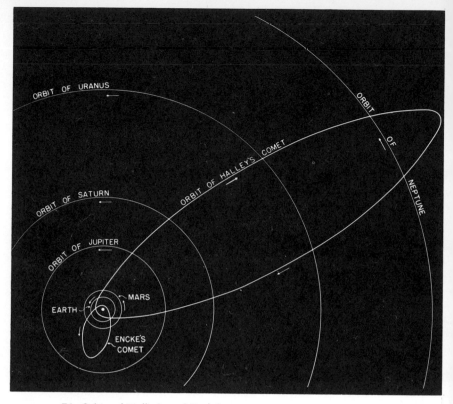

74. Orbits of Halley's and Encke's comets.

The idea that the speed of a body can be increased by friction is so contrary to our everyday experience as to seem ridiculous at first. It is true that some sort of resisting medium in space, by opposing its motion, does tend to make a body move more slowly. But there is an important difference between the effect of friction upon the motion of a body revolving around the sun and the effect of friction upon bodies moving at the surface of the earth. In space the instant the speed of a body decreases it immediately starts to fall inward toward the sun, thus diminishing the size of its orbit. Now we know that the closer a planet is to the sun the faster it moves. For example, Neptune moves with an average speed of 3.3 miles per second while Mercury at perihelion moves at 36

178

miles per second. In fact, a complete mathematical discussion shows that the speed lost by friction is more than made up by the speed gained from the shrinkage in the size of the orbit.

The successive returns of Encke's comet were in good agreement with the idea of a thin resisting medium near the sun, and by including a factor due to friction in his calculations, Encke was able to predict the time of perihelion passage very closely. Each time the comet came by the sun it showed a decrease of 0.11 days in its period of revolution. Since this was the only unusual thing in the comet's motion, and as it was in exact agreement with the way a resisting medium should act, Encke felt there was strong evidence for the existence of such a medium. But he was also careful to point out that no similar comparison had been made for any other comet of short period, and that such a comparison was highly desirable.

After Encke's death in 1865 at the age of seventy-four, the task of predicting the motion of the comet was taken up by von Asten at the Poulkovo Observatory, outside St. Petersburg, Russia. His troubles began at once, for at its very next return in 1868 the change in speed, which had been so steady in Encke's time, suddenly decreased by half, while when the comet returned in 1871 it appeared to have vanished entirely! The action of the comet was so different from its earlier behavior that von Asten decided the only thing to do was to start again from the beginning by investigating each of the eighteen observed returns from 1819 to 1875. His results only confirmed those that Encke had obtained before, that there was a gradual acceleration in the motion of the body produced by a constant resistance in space, which for convenience of calculation he supposed acted only when the comet was nearest the sun. On this basis he was able to represent the comet's motion in a satisfactory way except for the altogether unexplained absence of the acceleration in 1871. The only explanation he could think of was that the comet had undergone some violent disturbance in June of 1869 when it was about 300 million miles from the sun, such as a collision with an asteroid. A search showed that the comet had passed within 6 million miles of the asteroid Diana in May, but this at most could scarcely have accounted for more than 1 per cent of the slowdown in its motion that was observed. Von Asten's work was cut short by his death in 1878 at the age of thirty-six.

The work was continued by Oskar Backlund of the Poulkovo Observatory, who found the problem in a most unsatisfactory condition. The motion of the comet from 1871 to 1881 clearly indicated that the idea of a constant resistance in space which Encke and von Asten had assumed no longer held. In fact, the whole matter seemed in such a confused state that he decided—as von Asten had done before him—to start all over from the 1819 beginning.

Backlund's first step was to find out exactly how much disturbing effect the planets Mercury, Venus, earth, Mars, Jupiter, and Saturn had had on the comet from 1819 to 1891, which was a considerable undertaking in itself. Once he had rid the orbit of the disturbing effects of the planets, he was able to show that it was impossible to represent the motion of the comet by any single assumption. Instead it was necessary to divide the interval into three distinct periods. During the first, from 1819 to 1858, the change in speed was nearly constant; in the second, from 1858 to 1871, the change in speed diminished; while in the last, from 1871 to 1891, the change in speed had remained nearly constant but with about 60 per cent of its 1819–1858 value. In addition, Backlund was able to prove what von Asten during his short life had only suspected, that the resisting medium acted chiefly when the comet was nearest the sun.

Backlund carried out his work on the motion of the comet with such perseverance and success that in 1909 he was awarded the gold medal of the Royal Astronomical Society. After his death in 1916 the Poulkovo Observatory continued to make predictions for each return of the comet, a project which this observatory has now been doing for ninety years. Their calculations held good until 1931, when the motion of the comet deviated widely from prediction, indicating that another mysterious change had occurred.

After this disturbance, however, the times of perihelion passage by the sun for both 1935 and 1937 agreed closely with prediction. The next two returns, in 1941 and 1944, found the comet so faint and poorly situated for observation that scarcely any information was obtained about it. At its return in 1947 it was found a little farther from its predicted position than expected, and perihelion passage occurred about half a day earlier than predicted by Poulkovo.

180

Backlund thought the changes in the motion might be produced by brief collisions with a meteoritic ring near the sun, the abrupt effect being due to the changing thickness of the ring. Whipple has shown that the Taurid meteors some ten thousand years ago were associated with Encke's comet, so that it has been revolving around the sun practically in its present orbit for at least this long and probably much longer. Against the idea of a resisting medium is the fact that other short-period comets do not show a change of pace like Encke's—but then none come nearly so close to the sun as Encke's.

Backlund also gave serious consideration to the possibility that the change in speed might be due to something coming from the sun itself. He pointed out that large errors in the predicted times of perihelion passage in 1828, 1838, and 1848 occurred in years of high sunspot activity. Also, the first abrupt change in 1858 was near the sunspot maximum of 1860, as well as others in 1868, 1895, and 1905. And the most recent large deviation in 1931 was supposed to be due to a change when the comet was close to the sun in 1928, which also was a year of sunspot maximum. On the other hand, nothing unusual seems to have occurred when the comet passed close to the sun in 1918 and 1921, although 1918 was a year of high sunspot activity.

Thus the motion of Encke's comet still cannot be explained simply by the law of gravitation alone. But whether the peculiarities in its motion will finally be found to originate in meteoritic collisions near the sun, in solar emanations from the sun, or some other source, it is impossible to say at present.

▶ *What are shooting stars?*

Shooting stars are not, of course, really "shooting stars." The stars are great suns similar to our own but so far away they have shrunk in size until they appear as mere points of light in the sky. Shooting stars actually are tiny particles, often no larger than a pebble or a grain of sand, that fly into the atmosphere about 70 miles up with speeds as high as 45 miles a second. Then by their friction with the atmosphere they become so hot that they flash across the sky as a momentary streak of light. The particle does not just glow like a spark from a chimney. Rather the air particles all along the path of the meteor are made to glow as the meteorite flies past them at high speed, in somewhat the same way that neon gas glows in an electric sign. The meteor's light might also be compared to that of the aurora borealis. Heat is not the only form of energy that can be transformed into light. That is the reason such a small particle can produce so much light. The air particles all along the path of the meteor are set glowing, not just the light from the particle itself.

▶ How big are meteorites?

First we should carefully distinguish between a *meteor* and a *meteorite*. A meteor is simply the flash of light we see in the sky. It is purely a visual effect. The meteorite is the body that produces the light. We never see a meteorite except those large enough to survive their trip through the atmosphere and land on the surface of the earth. Meteorites are all sizes, from great boulders weighing many tons down through particles the size of

75. Meteor crater in Arizona, believed to have been caused by impact of a huge meteorite.

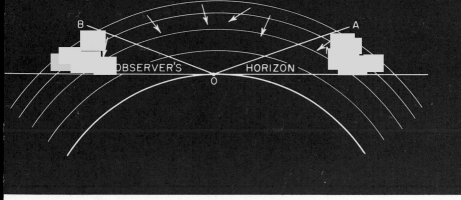

76. Meteors are visible only in the small part of atmosphere above the observer's horizon. Also, due to obscuration, meteors are not visible at horizon but only above sky formed by lines *AOB*.

pebbles to micrometeorites so small they can only be detected under the microscope. This micrometeoritic dust has been collected by the United States Air Force at altitudes above 50,000 feet. It is fortunate for us that the earth has a protective atmospheric shield. Otherwise we should be directly exposed to the impact of these particles which, in the case of the larger ones, would knife through us like a bullet. This is what would happen on the moon where the airless surface is exposed directly to meteoritic bombardment. Just how serious this danger is nobody knows for sure. It has been estimated that a million meteorites land on each 400 million square feet of the moon per day. Imagine that we have an astronomical observatory with a reflecting telescope 300 inches in diameter. A telescope of this size would have an area of nearly 500 square feet. Hence, the probability that a meteorite would strike an area equal to that of our telescope on any day is roughly 1/800,000. Or expressed in another way, we would expect the telescope mirror to be hit once every 800,000 days on the average. These figures sound reassuring, but we still have an uneasy feeling the situation may not be quite so favorable as it appears on the surface. Working outdoors on the moon would be like being continually exposed to snipers' bullets without having any way of retaliating or taking cover.

183

On a clear, moonless night possibly ten meteors may be seen by careful watching. An observer is able to view only a small portion of the sky at one time, as can be seen from Figure 76. When we remember that we miss many meteorites that fall near the horizon, the number visible from one station is very small indeed. It has been estimated that the small number we see in a night actually represents a total all over the earth of 70 million meteors bright enough to be seen by the naked eye. The total mass of meteorites striking the surface of the earth in one day is only about a ton.

▶ *Why are more meteors seen in the morning than in the evening?*

More meteors are seen in the morning than in the evening for the same reason that more raindrops strike the windshield of a car than the back window. In the morning the observer is on the front or advancing side of the earth in its motion through space so that it meets the meteorites head-on. In the evening the observer is on the rear side of the earth and the only meteors he sees are those that overtake the earth from behind. For this reason we see about twice as many meteors per hour after midnight as before midnight. In addition, the apparent velocities of the meteor trails are higher after midnight than before.

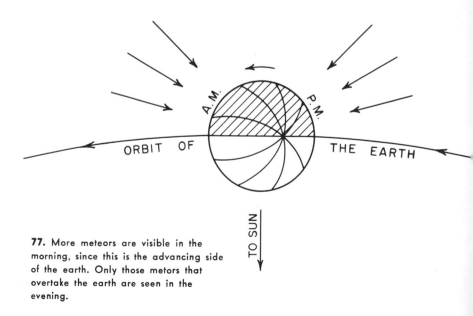

77. More meteors are visible in the morning, since this is the advancing side of the earth. Only those metors that overtake the earth are seen in the evening.

At some times of the year one may observe many more meteors than are observed on an average night. We say that we are having a meteoric shower. The name is rather misleading; very seldom do meteors come down fast enough to give the impression of an actual shower. If the trails of the meteors are carefully observed and plotted on a chart they will appear to meet at a common point called the radiant of the shower. That is, the meteors seem to be issuing from a rather small, particular part of the sky. This effect is purely an illusion. Actually the meteors are traveling toward the observer in nearly parallel lines. They only *seem* to diverge from a common point in the same way that railroad tracks seem to diverge from a point in the distance.

In 1866 the Italian astronomer Giovanni Schiaparelli made the totally unexpected discovery that the meteors from certain showers he studied were traveling around the sun in the same paths as several well-known comets. His work has been greatly extended since then and it is now believed that practically all meteors are of cometary origin. We get a meteor shower when the earth crosses the path in space of a comet. The comet has left a trail of meteoritic debris or rubbish in its wake so that eventually it becomes strewn along its entire path around the sun. Whenever the earth crosses this path it encounters more meteors than usual and we have a "shower." Once in a long time the meteors do fall fast enough to give the impression of a real shower. Thus after midnight on November 12, 1833, meteors were said to have fallen like snowflakes, 200,000 being visible within a few hours at some places. These meteors all seemed to be radiating from a point in the constellation of Leo, and as they streamed out "made the sky look like an umbrella."

One of the best showers visible recently in the United States occurred on the evening of October 9, 1946, when the earth encountered a swarm of particles in the wake of Comet Giacobini–Zinner, as had been predicted earlier. The meteors fell at the rate of about half a dozen per minute and were easily visible in a moonlit sky. The shower began early in the evening and was all over by midnight. The earth again passed near this meteoric swarm in 1959.

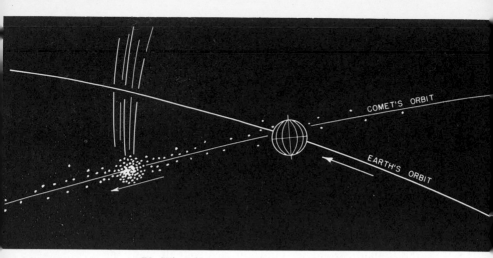

78. When the earth passes through the debris left in the wake of a comet we have a "meteoric shower."

79. Meteors *seem* to diverge from a central point in the same way that rails seem to diverge from a point in the distance. Actually, meteors are traveling toward observer in parallel lines.

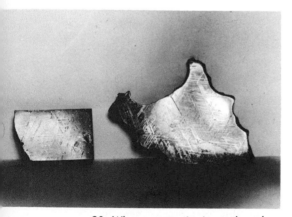

80. When a meteorite is cut through and the polished surface etched with acid, certain characteristic figures appear which identify it as a meteorite.

A shower of meteors is named from the constellation from which it appears to come. So we speak of the Perseids, the Leonids, the Lyrids, and so forth. In this table is a list of some of the principal meteor showers and the comets with which they are associated:

Meteoric showers

Name	Approximate date	Associated comet	Period of comet
Lyrids	Apr. 20	1861–I	418 years
Aquarids	May 6	Halley's	76
Perseids	Aug. 12	Swift's 1862–III	123
Draconids	Oct. 9	Giacobini, 1900	6.5
Leonids	Nov. 14	Tempel's, 1866–I	33

▶ *Where do meteors come from?*

We can tell whether a meteor belongs to the solar system or comes from interstellar space by measuring its velocity in relation to the sun. A vast improvement in measuring meteor velocities has been introduced by radio scientists in America and England, using what is called the "whistling meteor technique." A radio with a loudspeaker can be used to give a sound like a whistle whenever a meteor shoots across the sky, whether or not the sky is covered by clouds. The whistle, properly interpreted, measures the velocity with which the meteor is traveling, and with other radio measurements tells also its position, direction of travel, and altitude above the earth.

To find the velocity of a meteor in relation to the sun, we have to make a correction for its motion with respect to the earth. The earth is revolving around the sun at a speed of 18.5 miles per second. Suppose a meteorite is moving with a speed of 30 miles per second, relative to the sun. If the earth meets it head-on they will collide with a velocity of 48.5 miles per second. On the other hand, if the meteor overtakes the earth they will collide with a speed of only 11.5 miles per second.

The speed of the meteor (relative to the sun) determines whether it belongs to the solar system or comes from interstellar space. It all depends upon whether or not the meteor has a velocity greater or less than 26 miles per second. At the distance of the earth from the sun this is known as the critical velocity or "velocity from infinity." If at the earth's distance the meteor is moving faster than 26 miles per second, the sun will not be able to hold it with its gravitational field, and the meteorite will fly out of the solar system, never to return. But if it is moving less than 26 miles per second, the sun's gravitational field is dominant and the body must move around the sun in an elliptical orbit.

Results obtained from the latest measurements of meteors indicate that nearly all of them are members of the solar system. Only about 1 per cent have velocities above 26 miles per second, indicating that they come from outer space. It is believed that practically all meteorites come from the debris of comets as they move around the sun and disintegrate. Thus meteorites originate in the same way comets do, whatever that is.

▶ What is the gegenschein?

The *gegenschein* (German: "counterglow") is a faint oval patch of light in the sky that may be some thirty times the size of the full moon. It has the distinction of having been discovered three times. The first time was in 1854 by a German astronomer named Theodore Brorson, who published a brief description of it. Evidently this went unnoticed, because in 1868 it was discovered again by T. W. Backhouse, an English astronomer. His announcement also apparently went unnoticed, for fifteen years later it was still practically unknown. One night in October, 1883, a young American astronomer, Edward Emerson Barnard, was searching the sky for comets with a small telescope when he happened to notice a curious patch of light near the constellation Pegasus. He supposed it was only a cloud, but the next night it was still there in about the same place. He watched it for several nights and found it was moving eastward among the stars at the rate of a degree a day, an angular distance in the sky equal to twice the diameter of the full moon. This is the same direction and rate that the sun moves in the sky owing to the motion of the earth around it. Also, the object was directly opposite the·sun in the sky. Barnard at that time was only an amateur astronomer just starting his career. He sent his observations to a professional astronomer asking for information. Back came the answer: He had discovered the *gegenschein*—for the third time!

Since then the gegenschein has been observed by many different astronomers. It has been photographed and the intensity of the glow measured with the photoelectric cell. According to Barnard's account, it is not really difficult to see. In fact, he remarked that there are few things in the sky easier to see than the gegenschein.

The gegenschein makes an ideal object for amateurs to study, since no telescopic equipment is required. Any magnification reduces the contrast of the glow against the night sky, thus blotting it out completely. The main essential is that there must be no moon and no artificial lights nearby. It is invisible in June and July, probably because then it falls in the Milky Way. It is most conspicuous in September and October, when it falls in a dark part of the sky. The best way to look for the gegenschein is by glancing at the place it is supposed to be by averted vision, out of the corner of the eye. Strangely enough, Barnard said that he could see the gegenschein about as well in a hazy sky as on the clearest, darkest night. Also, he always had the impression that the gegenschein was not very far away, in the atmosphere rather than in outer space.

What is this ghostly companion of the earth?

Nobody knows. According to one hypothesis it consists of particles expelled from the earth's atmosphere in the same manner that particles are expelled from the tail of a comet. If this is true, then the earth has a tail projecting behind it away from the sun like the tail of a comet. Another suggestion is that the gegenschein consists of an immense swarm of meteorites at a distance of 930,000 miles from the earth in the opposite direction from the sun. It can be shown mathematically that the gravitational attractions of the earth and sun would produce a condensation of meteorites at this position. As meteorites approach this region they are caught in a sort of dynamic whirlpool, but after staying there for a while and performing a few revolutions, they escape and continue on in their orbits.

It is too bad that no observations of the gegenschein were scheduled during the International Geophysical Year. What is needed most of all are simultaneous observations of the gegenschein from stations several thousand miles apart, which would allow the

189

distance to be determined. Whatever the explanation of the gegen-schein may be, after a hundred years it is still one of the least understood of all the large, easily observable objects in the sky.

▶ Where did the planets come from?

This is a fascinating subject which has engaged the minds of men from earliest times. Many possibilities have been suggested, ranging from the myths of ancient times to the various hypotheses of the present day. But since the solar system apparently originated several billion years ago, and since nobody was around when it happened, it is doubtful if we can ever be sure we have found the right answer. All we have to go on is the way the sun and planets look *today*. How they looked several billion years ago is pretty much a matter of guesswork.

One of the most successful hypotheses of the origin of the planets was that put forward by the great mathematician Pierre Simon Laplace, at the end of a popular book on astronomy which he wrote about 1800. There is no evidence that Laplace ever took his own hypothesis at all seriously. In fact, he remarked that it was advanced "with that distrust which everything ought to inspire that is not the result of observation or of calculation." Yet this product of his lighter moments, which he doubtless tossed off with hardly a second thought, probably gained wider acceptance than any other theory in the history of science. Indeed, for practically a century it was accepted almost without question. Darwin's theory of the origin of species aroused a storm of controversy. But everybody liked Laplace's nebular hypothesis.

Laplace started by assuming that the solar system originally consisted of a vast discus-shaped mass of gas at high temperature which was rotating slowly in the direction in which the planets now revolve in their orbits. As this mass of gas lost heat by radiation into space, it cooled. As the mass cooled it also shrank; owing to this shrinkage it had to rotate faster. This effect is seen when a skater spinning on one foot with his arms extended wraps them around his body. When he moves his arms he spins more rapidly. That is, a spinning body has a certain quantity of rotation (*angular momentum,* as it is called in technical language), and so long as the spinning body is not acted upon by outside forces, this

190

quantity of rotation remains the same. As the rotating mass of gas continued to shrink and rotate faster there came a time when the centrifugal force at its edge became equal to the force of gravitation acting inward, and when this happened a ring of matter was left behind at the equator. The mass continued to contract until eventually another ring was left off, and another and another, as many rings being sloughed off as there are planets in the solar system. These rings would hardly be the same size all the way around. One part would be larger than the rest and this would gradually attract the remainder of the ring to it. This mass of gas formed from the rings is the material from which a planet condenses. The planetary nebula would itself shrink also, leaving rings which condensed into satellites. The sun is all that now remains of the great discus-shaped mass of gas that once filled the solar system out to the orbit of Pluto and beyond.

Laplace's nebular hypothesis also probably gained wide acceptance because it was so easy to visualize. You could almost see the main mass of the nebula shrinking, leaving off rings which condensed into planets, which in turn left off rings which condensed into satellites. So long as you didn't examine things too carefully it was a most satisfying theory. By 1925, however, there were so many objections to the nebular hypothesis that astronomers reluctantly had to abandon it. To mention only a few, it fails to take into account objects such as the asteroid Icarus, which has an orbit extending from inside the orbit of Mercury to beyond the orbit of Mars. On the Laplacian hypothesis the orbits of all the objects in the solar system should be nearly circular. Also, the planets and their satellites should all revolve in the same direction —yet several satellites of the giant planets revolve in a retrograde direction. Finally, the planet Jupiter, which constitutes only one tenth of 1 per cent of the mass of matter in the solar system, possesses 98 per cent of its total quantity of rotation interior to the orbit of Saturn. Furthermore, instead of leaving off definite rings it seems more likely that the contracting nebula would leave off a thin disk of particles along its edge. Also, even if a gaseous ring were left off there is doubt that it could ever contract into a planet. It would be more likely to dissipate gradually into space, for the force of gaseous expansion would be much greater than the feeble mutual gravitation of its parts.

Following the abandonment of the nebular hypothesis, various catastrophic theories of the origin of the solar system were advanced, in which the planets were assumed to be formed by the close approach or collision of two stars. We know that even the moon—as small and far away as it is—raises tides upon the earth. Think how much more enormous such tides would be, produced by the approach of a star to within a few million miles of the sun. There would not be merely a tidal bulge produced; the effect would be more like a waterspout. Imagine such a tide, or spout, of dense gases being drawn out of the sun in the general direction of the passing star. Some of the raised material would be carried off into space with the passing star. Some of it would fall back into the sun. A large part, however, would break up into planets and continue to circle around the sun at varying distances but nearly all in the same plane. There would also be a good deal of scattered material which would form the comets and meteorites.

In a later modification of the encounter theory it was supposed that the sun was originally a double star, and that the passing star struck not the sun but the *companion* of the sun. The colliding stars would have gone off at very different angles, dragging out a long filament of torn star material between them. It is assumed that the two colliding stars and most of the material between them was carried away from the sun into space, but that enough remained near the sun to condense into planets.

The chief weakness of encounter theories is that the stars are so far apart that collisions between them must be exceedingly rare events. On this basis, planetary systems must be very scarce articles indeed. Also, the material torn out between the colliding stars would be subject to oppositely directed pulls from intruder and companion, so that instead of condensing into planets it is much more likely that it would have been torn apart into small fragments. Furthermore, gas torn from the interior of a star at a temperature of several million degrees would practically explode, forming a nebulous envelope around the two stars. The probability that planets would ever form out of such unpromising material seems very remote indeed.

The theory most often quoted at present reminds us somewhat of the nebular hypothesis. It assumes that the sun in condensing, possibly from an interstellar globule, acquired a dust cloud having a mass about one tenth the sun's mass. This dust cloud became concentrated into a flat disk in the present position of the planetary orbits. This cloud of gas, instead of rotating calmly about its center of gravity as in the Laplacian hypothesis, had many eddy currents within it, so that it was in a state of violent turbulence. These eddy currents would be unequal in size but on the average should increase with increasing distance from the sun. Fluctuations in density of the eddies would occur in which the more massive ones would devour the less massive. Finally a system of potential planets or "protoplanets," one for each of the planets of the solar system, would be left at approximately their present distances from the sun. The protoplanets might have had disks around them from which the satellites were formed.

It should be emphasized that there is no theory of the origin of the solar system that has won general acceptance today as Laplace's nebular hypothesis did in its time. All involve difficulties that are hard to explain away. But as famous geophysicist Harold Jeffreys remarked, "the problem confronting us is not one of seeking a nice convincing way in which the planets might have originated. Rather it is to explain the fact that the solar system exists at all. The most promising schemes have been tried and found wanting. Now we must turn to those that are highly improbable."

10 ▶ A SURVEY OF THE STARS

▶ *What are the stars?*

The stars are suns similar to our own, but so far away that they have shrunk until they appear in the sky as mere points of light. It happens that the star nearest the earth is of exactly the same type as the sun. This star, called Alpha Centauri, is four light years away or 270,000 times as distant as the sun. So by looking at this star we can see how the sun would look at the same distance. It is only because the sun is so near that it shows a disk in the sky. If we imagine the sun to move away from the earth its disk would gradually shrink until finally it too would appear as a point of light. Even in the most powerful telescopes the stars are so far away that they still appear as points of light.

▶ *Why are some stars brighter than others?*

The stars differ in their apparent brightness because they are at different distances from the earth and because they differ widely in luminosity. A bright light at a great distance appears faint. A faint light quite near may appear bright. Looking at the stars, we have no way of telling whether they are near or far or how bright they are. We measure the brightness of a star by its magnitude. In 1850 a scale of magnitudes was chosen, establishing that a difference of 1 magnitude between two stars meant that one is 2.5 (2.512 exactly) times as bright as the other. This makes a bright star of magnitude 1 just 100 times as bright as a star of magnitude 6, which is about the faintest visible to the unaided eye. The magnitude scale can be extended in either direction to brighter or fainter stars as far as we please. The *smaller* the number representing the magnitude of a star, the *brighter* the star is. It works something like your golf score: the smaller your score, the better player you are. As we have just seen, a star barely visible to the naked eye is of magnitude 6. A fairly bright star like Betelgeuse, the big red star in the constellation Orion, is of about magnitude 1. A still brighter star would be of magnitude zero (0.14, to be precise) like Vega, the bright blue star in the constellation Lyra. But we can go below zero to still smaller or negative numbers. Thus Sirius, the brightest-appearing star in the sky, is of magnitude -1.5. The planet Venus is of about magnitude -4. The sun has an apparent magnitude of about -27. On the other hand, the faintest star that can be photographed with the 200-inch telescope is of about magnitude 22.5. When we try to express the luminosity of stars not in magnitudes but in mathematical terms of how much brighter one is than another, we run into figures of staggering size. Thus Sirius is about 4000 million times as bright as the faintest stars we can photograph. And the sun appears to be 10,000 million times as bright as Sirius.

We cannot tell anything about the *real* brightness of the stars until we know their distance. We know the law relating the brightness of a light with distance: The brightness varies inversely as the square of the distance. That is, if we double the distance of a star it appears one fourth as bright. If we treble the distance it appears one ninth as bright. Therefore, if we know how bright a star appears at a certain distance we can calculate how bright it would appear at any other distance. Suppose we know the distance of some lights of different candlepower. We measure their apparent brightness with a sensitive light-recording instrument or photometer. We still don't know their actual brightness on account of their different distances. If the lights were all at the *same* distance we could tell immediately which ones are actually the brightest. It would be extremely difficult if not impossible to put them all at the same distance and then measure their apparent brightness. But there is really no necessity for doing so, because if we know their apparent brightness at different known distances, from the inverse square law we can readily calculate their apparent brightness at some common distance, say of 10 miles. We might call their magnitude at 10 miles their absolute magnitude, since it tells us the real or absolute brightness of the lights in relation to one another. That is, a 200-watt light bulb would be twice as bright as a 100-watt bulb, and four times as bright as a 50-watt bulb.

195

81. Diffuse nebulosity around Merope in the Pleiades. The stars in this photograph differ in brightness both because of distance and actual luminosity.

We can apply the same principle to the stars. If we know the distances of some stars and measure their apparent brightness, then we can calculate how bright they would appear at some common distance and thus find their true relative brightness or absolute magnitude. But first we must measure the distances to the stars. And the stars are so far away that this is very difficult to do.

▶ How are distances to the stars measured?

Before considering how the distance to a star is measured, let us consider how some difficult-to-measure distance on the earth is calculated, since the principle is the same in both cases. Such distances may be found by measuring the *difference in direction* in which an object is seen from two places some distance apart. Suppose two surveyors want to measure the distance across the Grand Canyon. They set up their instruments at some carefully measured, known distance apart, such as AB in Figure 82. This is called the base line. Then the surveyor at A measures the angular distance between some point on the opposite bank such as P and the position of point B. This angle PAB we will call angle A. Then the surveyor at B measures the angle between P and point A. This angular distance PBA we will call angle B. Now, knowing the

82. *Above:* The base line AB is measured carefully. Then surveyors measure the angles at A and B. Knowing the length of AB, and the angles A and B, the distance across the chasm can be calculated.

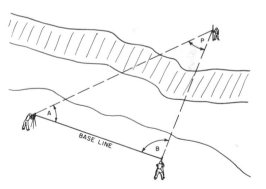

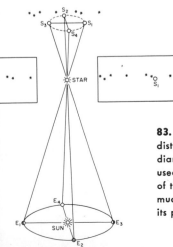

83. *Left:* in measuring the distance to the stars the diameter of the earth's orbit is used as a base line. The shift of the nearer star in relation to much more distant stars gives its parallax.

197

angles at *A* and *B* and their distance apart, it is possible from trigonometry to calculate the distance across the chasm *AP* or *BP*.

The angular width of *AB* as seen from *P* is called the parallax of *AB*. Although the parallax is not measured directly it can be found as soon as the two angles *A* and *B* are known.

It should be obvious that to measure the distance across the chasm accurately the surveyors should have a fairly long base line. That is, if they want to measure a distance about 10 miles wide they should have a base line of at least a mile. Otherwise the difference in direction of *P* as seen from *A* and *B* will be so small that the distance *AP* or *BP* found from it may be in serious error.

On the earth it is easy to make the base line as long as we want. But it is quite different in measuring distances to the heavenly bodies. In measuring the distance to the planets we can use the whole earth, 8000 miles wide, as our base line. But the stars are so far away that such a base line is far too short. It would be worse than trying to measure the distance across a 10-mile chasm using a base line of an inch. Instead we use the whole width of the earth's orbit in space, which is 186,000,000 miles wide from one point to the point where the earth is opposite six months later. Even this great distance is so small compared with the distances of the stars that only a few thousand of the nearest can be measured by this direct or trigonometric method. The only wonder of it is that astronomers can measure such small parallaxes with assurance at all. Even measuring the distance to the nearest star is like looking at a point 50 miles away through a window two feet wide, first out of one side and then out of the other.

In practice, all parallax work today is done by photography. The astronomer selects a star which for some reason he thinks is fairly close to the earth. Near this star are other, faint stars in the field of view of his camera which are presumably so far away that they have no parallax. Now the astronomer measures the position of the star in which he is interested in relation to these faint stars. On the photographic plate when first measured it will appear among these stars as in Figure 83. Then, six months later, when the earth is on the other side of its orbit, he measures the position of this star again in relation to the faint stars. Owing to the displacement of the earth in its orbit, the star will not appear at quite the same position it did six months ago but will appear to have

198

shifted its position slightly among the stars, as shown in Fig. 83. Of course, many more than two observations of the star are necessary in actual practice. By measuring the slight shift in position of the star on the photographs, and knowing the length of the base line, the parallax of the star can be found, and from the parallax its distance from the earth.

▶ How are distances to the stars expressed?

The stars are so far away that it is very awkward to express their distances in miles. For example, the distance to the nearest star is 25,000,000,000,000 (25 trillion) miles. Such numbers are so big and cumbersome to write that they have no meaning for us. It is like trying to express the distance across the United States in inches. The unit that is in most general use is probably the *light year*. The light year, as its name indicates, is the distance that light travels in a year, at a speed of 186,000 miles per second. It is a distance equal to 6,000,000,000,000 miles. Measured in this unit the distance to the nearest star is 4.3 light years.

It may surprise you to hear that, although astronomers go to a great deal of time and trouble to measure the parallax of a star, they are not particularly interested in its distance from the earth. At least that is not their primary interest. As we have already seen, once we know the distance to a star we can calculate its true candlepower or absolute magnitude. Thus Sirius, the brightest star in the sky, *appears* to be six times as bright as Rigel. But is Sirius really brighter than Rigel or is it just that Sirius is closer to us? We cannot tell until we know their distances. As it turns out, Sirius is a comparatively close star, only 8.7 light years distant, while Rigel is 650 light years distant. This means that actually Rigel is an extremely luminous star, 23,000 times brighter than the sun, while Sirius is only 23 times as luminous. Thus a knowledge of the distances of the stars is only another way of gaining something much more important about them—a knowledge of the constitution of the stars themselves.

▶ What is the parsec?

Astronomers have another unit they use in expressing the distance of the stars which they prefer to light year. This unit is called the *parsec*. We saw that the parallax of a star is the angle at the star subtended by the radius of the earth's orbit. A star that has a parallax of 1″ (one second) of arc is at a distance of 1 parsec. This is a very small angle, so small that with the unaided eye we cannot possibly detect such a difference in the distance of two bodies separated by this amount. About the smallest angle we can hope to detect without optical aid amounts to a few minutes of arc. (One 1′ [one minute] of arc is sixty times 1″ of arc). One parsec is equal to 3.26 light years. The feature about the parsec that makes it so handy for the astronomer is the ease with which the distance of a star can be expressed in this unit. You simply divide the parallax of the star into 1 and the result is its distance in parsecs. Thus if a star has a parallax of half a second of arc, 0.5″, it is at a distance of 2 parsecs. If it has a parallax of 0″.1, or one tenth of a second of arc, it is at a distance of 10 parsecs.

Astronomers have agreed to call the magnitude a star would have at a distance of 10 parsecs (32.6 light years) its absolute magnitude. Thus, by comparing the absolute magnitudes of stars we can tell their real relative brightness or candlepower.

▶ *Why are the stars different colors?*

It might be thought that the stars appear different colors because of the chemicals they contain. This is the reason fireworks show different colors. Chemicals heated to incandescence give off certain spectral rays so strongly that some of them glow with the light of a particular color. For example, the elements strontium and lithium emit red rays very strongly so that any substance containing these chemicals when highly heated shows a bright flash of red, a characteristic that furnishes an easy test for these elements. We have seen that the element sodium emits two yellow rays strongly. So if common table salt—which is sodium chloride—is tossed into a flame we get a bright yellow flash from these two spectral rays. There are other elements which emit green and blue rays when thrown into a flame.

Now a star like the sun contains many different elements, but these have nothing to do with the light of the sun—which is a yellowish white. Neither do red stars contain an abundance of strontium or lithium. The color of a star is determined entirely by

200

its temperature. We know that the higher the temperature of a body the brighter it appears. Not only does a body become brighter as its temperature rises but its color changes also. A piece of iron at low temperature glows a dull red. Heat it up and its color becomes cherry red, orange, yellow, until finally we say it is white-hot. Similarly, the tungsten filament in an electric-light globe shines with a bright white light because it is much hotter than the carbon filament in an old-fashioned light globe, which was at a much lower temperature and so was yellowish in color. Similarly, the stars appear different colors because they are at different temperautres. A star has to be rather bright to show distinct color. Only the twenty brightest stars show distinct coloration to the eye.

> ▶ *How are stars classified according to their temperature?*

We have seen that a star like the sun has many dark lines in its spectrum which were measured and named by Fraunhofer in 1814. In the latter half of the nineteenth century a few observers, notably such pioneers as Secchi, Lockyer, and Huggins, examined the stars with the spectroscope and attempted to classify them according to the dark lines they showed. The white stars showed only a few dark lines. The yellowish stars showed many lines, like the sun. The red stars showed still more lines; in fact, whole portions of their spectra were blotted out by series of dark lines or bands. This early work was very difficult because it had to be done visually, making it impossible to examine the spectrum of a star at leisure as may be done on a photograph. Later, when photography came into use and the spectroscope therefore became a spectrograph, it was possible to classify the spectra of the stars on a wholesale basis. Much of this work was done at the Harvard College Observatory, where a system of classification was gradually worked out by assigning letters to stars of different spectral types. Some of the original letters used were dropped until finally the system employed at present was worked out. It was found possible to arrange the stars in a *spectral sequence* which depended upon their temperature. The hottest stars of spectral types O, B, and A are white. Cooler stars of spectral types F, G, and K are yellowish. The very coolest stars (types M and N) appear red. Thus the spectral sequence from the hottest to the coolest stars runs O, B, A, F, G, K, M, N—easy to remember from the sentence "Oh, be a fine girl, kiss me now." The temperature of the stars of different spectral types runs roughly as shown in this table:

Spectral class	Typical star	Temperature (Fahrenheit)	Color
O	Zeta Puppis	60,000°	Blue-white
B	Epsilon Orionis	40,000	Blue-white
A	Sirius	22,000	White
F	Procyon	14,000	Yellowish-white
G	Sun	11,000	Yellow
K	Arcturus	8,000	Orange
M	Antares	4,000–6,000	Red
N	19 Piscium	4,000–6,000	Red

Even the coolest stars have high temperatures compared with the temperatures we ordinarily encounter upon the earth. The M and N stars look particularly red since so much of their spectrum in the blue and violet is absorbed by dark bands.

84. Relative sizes of stars of different types.

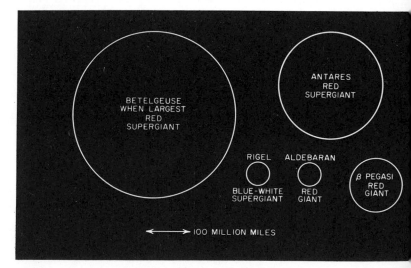

▶ What are giant and dwarf stars?

Astronomers have adopted some picturesque terms for describing the luminosity of the stars. Remember that the true luminosity of a star is measured by its absolute magnitude, the magnitude a star has at the distance of 10 parsecs or 32.6 light years. Stars with an absolute magnitude brighter than +1 are called giants. Stars of absolute magnitude fainter than +1 are called dwarfs. A few very luminous stars are called supergiants. The terms supergiant, giant, and dwarf apply strictly to the luminosity of the stars and only incidentally to their actual size, for some giant stars are bigger than the supergiants. But giants and supergiants are both larger than the dwarfs.

▶ How big are the stars?

We can see that the total luminosity or absolute magnitude of a star must depend upon both its size and temperature. A large star at a high temperature must emit more light than a small star at low temperature. But we can also conceive of a very large star at low temperature having a greater total brightness than a small star at high temperature. Or a small bright star might emit more light than a large cool star. Thus we see that the stars we call red giants must be real giants in size. They are of low surface temperature, yet their total luminosity as measured by their absolute magnitude is very high. On the other hand, a red dwarf star must be quite small. It is at the same surface temperature as the red giant but it has a low luminosity. The red giants are large bonfires but not very hot ones. The red dwarfs are small bonfires that also burn feebly. The high luminosity of the white giants must be due almost entirely to their high temperature. They are rather small bonfires that burn with an intensely hot flame. The very hot white stars are only roughly the size of the sun. The giant red stars are vastly larger.

▶ How is the size of the stars measured?

In the case of a few of the very largest stars it has been possible to measure their size directly with an instrument called an *interferometer*. It is beyond the scope of this book to

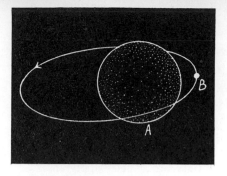

85. The system of the double star Epsilon Aurigae. This consists of a bright smaller star revolving around a huge invisible companion. Size of the stars can be estimated from length of time they are in eclipse.

attempt to explain how the interferometer operates. But with such an instrument attached to the 100-inch telescope in 1920 the angular diameters of several red giants were measured. The angular diameter merely gives us the apparent size of an object in the sky, not its real diameter in miles. For example, the apparent size of the sun and moon is the same—half a degree. We cannot tell their true size until we know their distances. Then we find that their size differs a great deal since the sun is so much farther away than the moon. Similarly, we cannot tell the real diameter of a star from its apparent diameter as measured with the interferometer. We must also know the parallax or distance of the star. Some of these red giants are so far away that their distances are not accurately known. Uncertain as we are of their distances, we know that they are tremendously large stars compared with the sun. For example, the red giant star Betelgeuse is so large the sun could be put in its center and there would be plenty of room left for the earth and Mars to revolve around it in their present orbits. Such stars have been called red-hot vacuums. Most of the material of the star is near its center. It has a small hot dense core at a temperature of 200 million degrees surrounded by a highly distended, relatively cool atmosphere. It is like a big bubble of gas that is mostly empty except for a hot nucleus at the core.

▶ How are sizes found from eclipsing stars?

We also have other ways of measuring the size of stars, in the case of two stars that are close together and revolving around each other. Sometimes these stars are moving in orbits that lie in or near our line of sight so that they eclipse each other regularly. Stars of this type are called eclipsing binaries. As the stars revolve around each other, moving alternately toward and away from the earth we can find their speed of orbital motion from the Doppler shift of the lines in their spectrum. The length of time required for the bright star to disappear behind the dark one and reappear gives us the size of the dark star. The time required for the bright star to disappear gives us its size. In this way the actual size of the two stars may be calculated from combined spectrographic and photometric observations of the system. A vast amount of information can be determined about stars by such observations. We can tell not only their size and mass but also their shape and the distribution of light over their surface.

It is from such observations that stars may be detected which otherwise would be wholly unknown to us because they are so faint. One of these is the star called Epsilon Aurigae, a system consisting of a small bright star revolving around a huge faint star at so low a temperature it is nonluminous. The diameter of this star has been calculated to be 2300 million miles, large enough so that the sun could be put in its center with room enough left over for Saturn to revolve around it.

The bright white stars are only a few times larger than the sun. They owe their high luminosity to their extreme temperatures rather than their large size. The red dwarfs are slightly smaller than the sun. An interesting group of stars are those called the white dwarfs. They are very small stars with a high surface temperature. These stars are no larger than the planets of the solar system, some no bigger than the earth. In this case their low luminosity is due to their minute size.

Thus we see that there is a great range in size among the stars of around 100,000 to 1, from the vastly extended red giants down to the tiny white dwarfs.

▶ *How do astronomers arrange the stars?*

We have seen that the stars differ enormously among themselves. The range in size is roughly 100,000 to 1. The range in luminosity is even greater. A star which has been assigned the brightest absolute magnitude is one called S Doradus, which has an absolute magnitude of -8.9. The faintest known star is one discovered about 1946 with an absolute magnitude of $+20$. This

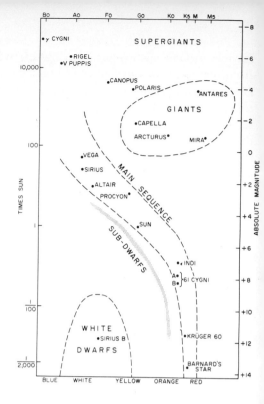

86. The Hertsprung-Russell (H-R) diagram for stars in the vicinity of the sun.

gives a range in real brightness between the two of 400 billion. The range in mass of the stars is not so great, about 6000 to 1. Thus we find a much greater range in brightness among the stars than we do among the electric lights that we see at night scattered over the landscape. Suppose we consider a representative sample of several hundred stars. Is there some way of arranging them so as to bring out any relations that exist among them? What we would like to do is form a sort of map showing how the stars as citizens of the sky are distributed over it.

Such a map or diagram was first prepared by two astronomers named Ejner Hertsprung and H. N. Russell, and for this reason is generally known as the Hertsprung–Russell diagram or simply the H–R diagram. In this diagram the stars are arranged according to

206

their luminosity or absolute magnitude and their color. Since, as we have seen, the color of a star is directly related to its temperature, and the temperature to its spectral type, we can also consider the H–R diagram to be a scheme for arranging the stars according to their luminosity and spectral type. It really does not make much difference what criteria we use, color, temperature, or spectral type, they are so closely related to each other.

Such a diagram as shown in Figure 86 is made by plotting the luminosities of the stars at the left, with the stars of low luminosity at the bottom, increasing upward through stars of moderate luminosity (like the sun) to the stars of very high luminosity. The color of the stars or their temperature or spectral type is plotted from left to right, with the hot white stars at the left, the yellowish stars in the middle, and the red stars at the extreme right.

When such a plot is made it is found that the stars do not fall at random over the chart but show preferences for certain portions much more than others. Most of the stars fall along a band running from the upper left part of the diagram and extending down to the lower right. This is called the main sequence. The sequence begins with the hot blue-white stars to the left at the top, extends through the sun, and on down through the faint red stars. As we have already noted, stars brighter than absolute magnitude $+1$ are called giants. Those fainter than $+1$ are the dwarfs. Stars brighter than about absolute magnitude -4 are called supergiants. At the extreme end of the dwarf branch the temperatures of the stars are only about 3300° F. If cooler stars exist they are too faint to be observed by present methods.

The normal red giants occupy a region to the right of the main sequence and below that of the supergiants. The white dwarfs have a region all to themselves on the extreme lower left-hand side of the diagram. There is a dearth of stars between the red giants and the white stars of the main sequence called the "Hertsprung gap." Stars on the main sequence are generally similar to the sun. They range from white stars of moderate luminosity down to the red dwarfs.

It should be emphasized that this is the kind of H–R diagram we get for stars near the sun. It is necessarily based upon stars quite close to us whose distances were determined mostly from direct measurement by the trigonometric method. Thus it is not a representative sample of stars in all parts of the sky.

▶ Do the stars move?

The stars have apparent motions which they all share, due to the rotation of the earth and the changing direction of the earth's axis in space. These do not change the positions of the stars in relation to one another. The outline of the constellations always remains the same. You could watch the Big Dipper for changes all your life and never notice the slightest difference in the configuration of the stars in it.

Yet the stars do move. But their motions are so small they cannot be detected merely from casual naked-eye inspection even in

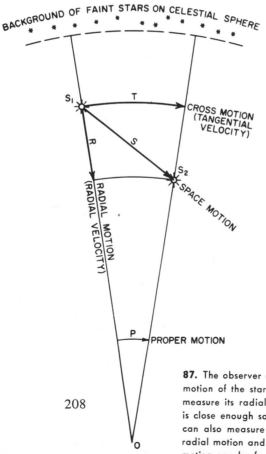

87. The observer at O measures the apparent angular pro motion of the star as it moves from S_1 to S_2. He can also measure its radial velocity with the spectroscope. If the st is close enough so that its distance can be determined he can also measure its cross motion in miles per second. It radial motion and cross motion known, the star's actual sp motion can be found.

the course of a lifetime. But with modern methods of measurement it is possible to detect the motion of some very fast-moving stars in only a few weeks. In most cases, however, the individual motions of the stars are so small they are extremely difficult or impossible to detect. This change in the position of a star is called its *proper motion*. It is measured in angular units or seconds of arc like the diameter of a planet. The proper motion does not of course give us the real motion of the star across the sky. The situation is shown in Figure 87. In relation to the earth, the star is moving along the line S from S_1 to S_2. Of course we cannot tell merely from looking at it whether it is moving toward or away from us. All we measure is its apparent angular motion across the line of sight.

We can also measure another motion of the star. This is its motion directly toward or away from us. We do this from the Doppler shift of the lines in its spectrum toward the red or violet. This gives us what is called its *radial velocity* in miles per second. If the star happens to be close enough so that we can get a reliable value for its distance we can also get its actual cross motion in miles per second. The radial motion and cross motion together give us the total or actual velocity of the star or what is called its *space motion*.

▶ How is the sun moving in space?

It should be evident that by measuring the proper motions and radial velocities of the stars we should be able to tell something about how the sun is moving in space. Suppose first of all for simplicity that all the stars are motionless and only the sun is moving. Then as the sun moves among them we should observe the same effect that would appear to a man walking through a forest, to use an oft-quoted example. As he moves forward the trees in front of him appear to be approaching him and moving farther apart. Those behind him are receding and seem to be closing together. Those to his right and left appear to be moving backward but show no motion toward or away from him. By studying the apparent motion of the trees he can tell which direction he is moving and how fast.

Or we might imagine ourselves on a ship at night steering a course among other ships. From the way the lights on the ships about us move we could tell a good deal about our own course. The ships would also be moving around us. Their apparent motions would be a combination of their actual motions with that of our own ship. From observations of these moving lights we could tell whether we were moving faster or slower than the average or just about the same.

Similarly, stars that lie ahead of the sun should on the average seem to be moving toward us and separating in the sky. Stars behind us should on the average appear to be receding and closing together. The stars in between should appear to be drifting backward but we should find no motion toward or away from us. This motion of the sun in space is called the "sun's way." The direction toward which the sun is moving in the sky is called the *solar apex*. The opposite direction in the sky is called the *antapex*.

As far back as 1783 Sir William Herschel made the first determination of the solar apex from the motions of thirteen bright stars, which gave a position within only some 10° of the best modern determination. Since then a vast amount of work has been done studying the motions and velocities of stars in our stellar system, which has given us a good picture of how the sun is moving in relation to the cloud of stars close by, and to our galactic system as a whole.

The motions of about 8000 stars comparatively nearby indicate that the sun is moving with a speed of 12 miles per second toward a point in the constellation of Hercules, about 1′ north of the fourth-magnitude star Omicron Herculis, within only 7′ of the star Lambda Herculis that Herschel found from only thirteen stars.

It should be emphasized that this is the motion of the sun in relation to a cloud of stars comparatively close by. As we shall see elsewhere, the sun has quite a different motion if its velocity is measured in relation to more distant stars.

88. The stars seem to be moving away from the point on the celestial sphere toward which the sun is moving (apex), and closing in on the opposite point (antapex).

210

11 ▶ SOME STARS THAT CHANGE IN BRIGHTNESS

▶ *What are variable stars?*

Early on the morning of November 10, 1942, Dr. Edison Pettit of the Mount Wilson Observatory went out in the front yard of his home in Pasadena to pick up the morning paper. It was early enough so that some of the brighter stars were still visible and, like most astronomers, Dr. Pettit glanced around the sky at the stars purely as a matter of habit. Ordinarily he would have picked up his paper and gone in the house to peruse the headlines, but this morning his glance around the sky revealed something unusual. Low in the south he noticed a bright object where ordinarily only third- and fourth-magnitude stars are visible. This object was brighter than first magnitude. Dr. Pettit knew at once that he had discovered what is called a new star or *nova*. Fortunately he had a six-inch telescope in his back yard with a sensitive light-measuring device or photometer attached to it. With this he was able to measure the magnitude of the star before it disappeared in the rising light of dawn. This was a rare case of the magnitude of a nova being measured before it reached maximum brightness, for the next night it was slightly brighter, being magnitude $+0.35$. After that it declined rapidly in brightness and by December 10 was invisible to the unaided eye.

A nova is a spectacular example of what we mean by a variable star. Novae are probably fairly common objects. The reason we see so few of them is that they appear without warning, and unless they happen to reach naked-eye visibility they do not force themselves upon our attention.

When we look at the stars casually they always appear to be of the same brightness. "The eternal stars" is a familiar expression.

211

89. The Crab nebula in the constellation Taurus is believed to be the remains of a nova or new star that appeared in A.D. 1054.

212

But if we measure the light of the stars with very sensitive instruments we find that many of them do *not* shine with a steady light; their brightness varies slightly. There are a few variable stars that were known before the invention of the telescope. One, called Mira the "Wonderful," whose variability was discovered in 1596, is in the southern constellation of Cetus. Mira is usually a star of moderate brightness of about magnitude 3.5, but it has been known to reach magnitude 1.5, when it briefly outshone all other stars in that part of the sky. At minimum brightness it sinks below naked-eye visibility to magnitude 9. Mira increases and decreases in brightness in an average period of 330 days, but it is very irregular, so that its brightening and fading may be early or late by 30 days.

Mira is a typical example of a group of stars whose light variation is so generally similar that they are called "Mira variables" or "long-period" variables. They are all red giants on the far right-hand side of the H–R diagram (Fig. 86). Their period of light variation ranges from 100 to 700 days. A class of stars akin to the Mira variables are the irregular variables, whose light changes are completely unpredictable. They also are red giants, the red star Betelgeuse or Alpha Orionis being a typical example. Their range in brightness is not so great as that of the Mira variables. Measures with the interferometer by means of which the changes in size of a star may be measured directly, indicate variations in the size of Betelgeuse ranging from 186 million to 280 million miles, or from about 200 to 300 times the diameter of the sun.

▶ *What are the Cepheid variables?*

This very important class of variable stars takes its name from the prototype in the constellation of Cepheus, a star of about the fourth magnitude designated by astronomers Delta Cephei, which was the first star of this type to be studied. Unlike the Mira variables, the Cepheids go through their light changes in a regular way in periods from a few days up to nearly 100 days. Their change in brightness is small compared with the Mira variables, being usually less than one magnitude. Most Cepheid variables are of type F and G. The Cepheid variables have probably been studied more intensively than any other stars in the sky. This is because there is a remarkable relation between their period of variation and their luminosity. The longer the period of the star the greater its real brightness or absolute magnitude.

This relationship, which is of tremendous importance in astronomy, was discovered by Miss Henrietta Leavitt while she was making a study of photographs of the Smaller Magellanic Cloud begun in 1906. In the southern hemisphere are two bright patches in the sky that look as if they might be parts of the Milky Way that had become detached from the main band. These are called the Magellanic Clouds after the great Portuguese navigator, Ferdinand Magellan. They are not clouds at all but vast aggregations of stars at a distance now estimated at 150,000 light years, although astronomers had no notion of their distance when Miss Leavitt first began her study of them. Her particular object was to detect variations in the intensity of the star images on plates taken of the Small Magellanic Cloud from a station in the southern hemisphere. It is hard to appreciate the magnitude or complexity of this task merely from reading about it. One is confronted by a plate over which are scattered seemingly countless little black specks, so thick in some places that they merge into a solid mass. A catalogue had to be made of the positions of these specks so each one could be identified later. Then the magnitude of the stars had to be determined on photographs of the Small Cloud taken at different dates. Upon first viewing one of these plates the enormity of the task makes it seem practically hopeless. Only by going about such work in a deliberate, systematic manner could one hope to get anything out of it.

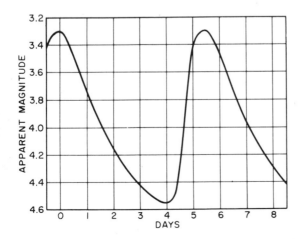

90. Light curve of the star Delta Cephei. The time from maximum light to the next maximum is about five days.

▶ *What is the period–luminosity relation?*

As might be expected, the results were slow in coming. One of the most interesting results that finally emerged from Miss Leavitt's study of the cloud was that the luminosity of the Cepheids in it depended upon their period. That is, the longer a Cepheid took to go through its light variation from one maximum to the next, the brighter it was. Cepheids that went through their light change rapidly were fainter. In fact, when the brightness or apparent magnitude of the Cepheids was plotted against their periods the result was a fairly smooth curve or *period–luminosity relation*. It should be noted that since the stars in the Small Magellanic Cloud are all at essentially the same distance, their relative brightness depended only upon their difference in apparent magnitude. That is, if one star *appeared* brighter than another it must actually *be* brighter since they are all at the same distance. Of course, if the distance of the cloud had been known it would have been possible to change the apparent magnitudes of the stars into absolute magnitudes. Then one would have known whether the Cepheids were very luminous stars like Rigel, or of moderate luminosity like Sirius, or about average brightness, like the sun.

It takes time to see the tremendous possibilities of the period–luminosity relation. But a little thought will show that it is a powerful means of measuring distance in space. Suppose that the period luminosity relation holds good for all Cepheids regardless of whether they occur in the Magellanic Cloud or in our own galaxy. If we could convert the apparent magnitudes in the period–luminosity relation into absolute magnitudes, we would have a means of measuring the distance of any group of stars that contains a Cepheid: all we would have to do would be to observe its period. Then, knowing its period, we could go to the period–luminosity relation and find its absolute magnitude. If we know both the absolute magnitude and apparent magnitude of a star we can calculate its distance at once. Thus from the period of a Cepheid— something *easy* to observe—we are able to get its distance—something *very difficult* to observe.

91. The Magellanic Clouds in the southern hemisphere.
Although they appear as clouds they are actually vast
aggregations of stars about 150,000 light years from the earth.

But before the apparent magnitudes on the period–luminosity curve could be changed to absolute magnitudes it was first necessary to determine the distance of at least one Cepheid. Knowing the distance and absolute magnitude of one Cepheid of a certain period, all the others would be immediately known. The trouble is that the Cepheids in our galaxy are all very distant stars so that it has been impossible to determine the distance of any of them by the direct trigonometric method. As a result, astronomers had to resort to an indirect statistical method which depended upon the proper motions of a number of Cepheids in our galaxy. In this way they found that eleven bright Cepheids gave an average absolute magnitude of -2.4 for a Cepheid with a period of six days. By this means the apparent magnitudes of all the Cepheids on the period–luminosity curve were converted into absolute magnitudes. Now astronomers had a means of finding the distance of any sort of group of objects, providing it contained a Cepheid variable whose period could be measured. Or so it seemed.

For after all the work done on the period–luminosity relation it has recently appeared that the determination of the distance of Cepheids from their proper motions is not so reliable as had been supposed. Therefore, while in principle the method remains as sound as ever, in practice it cannot be used since we still are unable to obtain an accurate value for the absolute magnitude of a single Cepheid.

For example, the distance to the Andromeda galaxy was formerly believed to be 750,000 light years, as determined from the Cepheid variables it contained. But when the Andromeda galaxy was first examined with the 200-inch telescope certain stars that were expected to appear could not be found. Evidently the galaxy is so far away that these stars are not bright enough to be observable. As a result, it was found that the Cepheids are about four times brighter than was originally supposed. And since the brightness of an object varies inversely with the square of its distance, this meant that the size of the entire universe outside the galaxy had to be doubled! Astronomers took this in stride but the general public was not so philosophic about it. They had always heard how accurately astronomers could measure things. Their faith was badly shaken when they found they had been off so badly on the size of the universe.

217

▶ What makes the Cepheids vary in brightness?

Out of several explanations that have been proposed the one most widely accepted today is the pulsation hypothesis. According to this idea the star alternately expands and contracts, the motion often being likened to that of a beating heart. Spectra of the Cepheids show a regular Doppler shift to red and violet, indicating that the surface of the star is actually approaching and receding as we would expect if it is undergoing pulsations. The highest velocity of approach occurs at maximum brightness and the greatest velocity of recession at minimum light. The star also undergoes a change in color with its period, being cooler and redder at minimum. The pulsation hypothesis accounts fairly well for the observed behavior of a Cepheid but still cannot be considered entirely satisfactory.

▶ What are cluster variables?

These are variable stars whose light variation closely resembles that of the Cepheids, except that it is much more rapid. Whereas the shortest time required for a Cepheid to run through its period of light change is about two days, the majority of cluster variables have periods of half a day. The one with the shortest known period, called CY Aquarii, has a period of only 88 minutes. It changes so fast that it doubles in brightness in 15 minutes! The two with longest periods are BQ Coronae Australis, with a period of 27 hours, and CE Herculis, with a period of 29 hours.

▶ Why are they called cluster variables?

These stars are called cluster variables because they were first discovered in globular star clusters and for several years none were known elsewhere. They were first found in a great globular star cluster called Omega Centauri, so far south that it can only be studied from the southern hemisphere. From a comparison of photographs of this cluster taken in 1895 at the southern station of the Harvard Observatory at Arequipa, Peru, dozens of variables were found which changed brightness in periods of from 7 to 20 hours, with rapid brightening and slower fading. Such stars had not been known to exist before.

218

A search of other globular clusters revealed more such variables, although some had none at all. But one globular cluster called Messier 3 was found to have 132 cluster variables out of 900 stars examined. Nearly all of the variable stars found in the other globular clusters had the same characteristics as those found in Omega Centauri. In 1900 a cluster variable was found outside a globular cluster. In a few years enough cluster variables were discovered outside clusters to outnumber those in the globular clusters. At present the number of cluster variables known is more than two thousand and is increasing rapidly.

Since more cluster variables are found outside clusters than in them the name no longer seems appropriate. Cluster variables now are often called RR Lyrae stars, from a star of the cluster type of the seventh magnitude with a period of thirteen hours. This is one of the brightest variables of this type known, and is one of the best-studied variables in the sky.

92. The globular cluster in Hercules, photographed with different exposure times. The very short period variable stars are found in clusters such as this one. Its distance is 34,000 light years.

▶ Why are cluster variables important?

The cluster variables are important as distance indicators. Early workers in this field noticed that wherever the cluster variables occurred they were always about the same apparent magnitude in relation to one another. That is, they might be sixteenth magnitude in one cluster, seventeenth in another, and fifteenth magnitude in still another. There was no appreciable range in brightness among the variables in the same cluster. This indicated that the cluster variables are probably all of the same absolute brightness, and that their differences in apparent brightness are simply the result of their different distances from the earth.

If, then, the cluster variables *are* all of the same brightness, the determination of the actual brightness of any one of them would determine the absolute magnitude of them all. The cluster variables are so far away that it has not been possible to measure the distance of a single one by the direct trigonometric method. But from a statistical study of their motions it has been found that the cluster variables are of absolute magnitude 0.0, with a luminosity 86 times that of the sun. With this information available we can find the distance of any object such as a star cluster or star cloud in which cluster variables occur. In this way the distances of the globular clusters that surround our galaxy on either side were measured. It is unfortunate that the cluster variables are not brighter; as it is they are too faint to show in the nearest galaxies, which apparently lie just beyond the reach of the 200-inch telescope.

Cluster variables may also be used to determine the magnitudes of other stars in the cluster. For example, the globular clusters contain the kind of stars we call "red giants." Suppose that the apparent magnitude of the cluster variables in a globular cluster is 15 and that of the stars identified from their spectrum as red giants is 13.5, or 1.5 magnitudes brighter. Since we know the absolute magnitude of the cluster variables is 0.0, then the absolute magnitude of the red giants must be -1.5. Now that we know the absolute magnitude of the red giants we can use them as distance indicators for globular clusters in which no variables occur. Also, since the red giants are a little brighter than the cluster variables, we can see them to somewhat greater distances.

220

12 ▶ THE "WHITE DWARFS"—
STARS OF HIGHEST DENSITY

▶ *What are the white dwarf stars?*

Sirius, the Dog Star, is the brightest-appearing star in the heavens, flashing in the winter sky like a brilliant blue-white diamond. Sirius is outstanding only because it happens to be so near the earth. Actually, it is a rather ordinary type of star. The most remarkable thing about Sirius is its companion, a star so faint that it requires a fairly good-size telescope to see it at all. And then the companion of Sirius, or Sirius B as it is called, is only visible when it is far enough from Sirius so that it is not blotted out in the glare of the brighter star. For many years Sirius B constituted such a puzzle to astronomers that it was one of the foremost mysteries of the sky. Even today, although the nature of stars like Sirius B is much better understood, the last word has not been said on the subject.

Sirius B was discovered August 31, 1862, by Alvin G. Clark, while he was testing out the lens for the 18-inch telescope of the Dearborn Observatory. Nearly twenty years before, however, its presence had been detected by the famous astronomer Bessel, through its gravitational pull upon Sirius and the irregularities it produced in the motion of the principal star. From his observations Bessel found that Sirius, instead of moving in a straight line at a uniform rate, was moving at a nonuniform rate in a wavy line. He concluded rightly that some unseen body of considerable mass was disturbing the motion of Sirius. From Bessel's observations the astronomer Peters calculated where the unseen body should be, and it was exactly in its estimated position that the faint eleventh-magnitude star was sighted by Alvin Clark. When further direct observations of Sirius B became available it was found to be revolving around Sirius in an orbit that required 50 years for a complete revolution.

The most remarkable and puzzling feature about the companion is that in spite of its extremely faint brightness, only about one ten-thousandth that of Sirius or one two-hundredth that of the sun, it is equal in mass to the sun and half as massive as Sirius itself. Yet photographs of the spectrum of the star showed that it is considerably hotter than the sun with a surface temperature of about 14,000° F. From its low luminosity we would expect it to be a red star of low temperature. Instead it is at such a high temperature that its surface is white! The only way we can account for its low luminosity is by assuming that the star is very small. For if it were a normal-size star it would shine with nearly the brightness of Sirius. Calculations based on its color, temperature, and absolute luminosity indicate that Sirius B is 24,000 miles in diameter—about the size of the planet Uranus. Yet it is as massive as the sun! This means there must be a great deal of matter crowded into a very small volume of space. In other words, the *density* of Sirius B is exceedingly high. In fact, it is 55,000 times as dense as water or 2600 times as dense as the metal platinum. The force of gravity on Sirius B is so great that if a man who weighs 150 pounds were transported to its surface he would weigh 2625 tons! He would be flattened out thinner than a pancake under his own weight. And the stuff of which this star is made is so heavy that you could not even lift a thimbleful of it, which would weigh about a ton.

▶ *How can Sirius B be so dense?*

We have every reason to believe that Sirius B, in spite of its high density, is gaseous from center to surface. But how can it be a gas when it is so dense? We think of it as being like a very hard, solid ball like a ball bearing. To understand how it is possible for material to be so dense and still gaseous, we have to consider the structure of the matter out of which it is made. We think of matter as being composed of very tiny particles called atoms, so small they are far beyond visibility in the most powerful microscope. You may think of each atom as consisting of a central nucleus which contains nearly all the mass of the atom. Whirling around the nucleus in orbits of different sizes are electrons, which are only about 1/1800 as massive as the nucleus. Most of the atom consists of empty space, the space around the nucleus formed by the whirling electrons. But the atoms cannot come too close to one another. They are restricted from approaching closer to one another than the distance bounded by their outer whirling electrons. That is, the orbits of the electrons cannot overlap or interlock.

But in a white dwarf star the matter is at such a high density that it is said to be in a "crushed" state, in which most of the electrons are stripped from their nuclei and no longer revolve around them in separate orbits. Instead, the electrons and atomic nuclei are closely mingled together, much closer than they could be in the gaseous or even solid state. You may think of the atoms as a group of men each whirling around himself a weight attached to a long cord. The men cannot approach closer than the length of the whirling weights. But now suppose the cord breaks and the weight flies away. Then a great many men and weights could be packed into a much smaller space than was possible before. Or you might think of the atoms in their normal state as being like Christmas-tree ornaments in a box. The ornament would take up a lot of space so that even though the box is filled it feels very light. But suppose you crushed the ornaments until they were ground to a powder. Now you could put a vast number of these crushed ornaments into a box, and if you packed the powder in tight enough it would be quite heavy. In roughly the same way we think of the matter in a white dwarf as being crushed so that the particles can come very close to one another, thus making it possible to reach densities of fantastic proportions.

In 1915 a spectrum of Sirius B was finally obtained which showed that the star was white and of a different spectral type from Sirius itself. This proved it was really a luminous body and not just a large planet reflecting light from Sirius. The fact that the star turned out to be white produced a revolution in astronomical thinking, because—as we have seen—astronomers knew immediately it must be very small. It is like a patch of snow on the side of a hill. The snow is much brighter than the hillside, but the total amount of light it reflects is much less because it is so small.

223

▶ How are white dwarfs found?

While the theoretical astronomers were wrestling with the problem of the high density of Sirius B, it was evident that it would be very desirable to see if more such stars could be found. As might be expected, their discovery was slow in coming owing to their low luminosity. After Sirius B was found to be white in 1915, seven years passed before another was tentatively identified as a white dwarf in 1922. The trouble was that the stars were so faint that it was impossible to reach them with the spectroscopic equipment then available. It became apparent that to find white dwarfs we should look for stars that are *faint,* and for which we also have a strong suspicion that they are *near.* As we have seen, it is an extremely long and laborious job to find the distance of a star by the trigonometric method. On the other hand, we can get an indication that a star is probably near from its proper motion. That is, we shall have the best chance of finding white dwarfs among faint stars that appear to be moving rapidly across the sky, since their rapid motion indicates they are close to us. Then, after finding a group of faint stars with large motion, the only thing that remains to be done is to determine whether they are red or white. This can be done by photographing them through color filters on plates sensitive to red and blue light. Such a program was started by W. J. Luyten in 1927, during the course of which some hundred million star images were examined. Of these only 3000 were found which satisfied both requirements of being faint and also having large motion. Of these 3000 candidates 2900 turned out to be ordinary red dwarfs. The remaining 100 were identified as white dwarfs. From this survey it appears that about 3 per cent of all the stars in a large volume of space are white dwarfs.

Several stars whose densities are much higher than that of Sirius B are now known. The most extreme case appears to be that of a star known only by its catalogue number: AC $+70°$ 8247. This star has been estimated to be only 4000 miles in diameter, about the size of the planet Mars. Its mass is the same as that of the sun, which makes its average density 10 million times that of the sun. A representative average specimen of the material of this star would have a density so high that a cubic inch would weigh 620 tons. A 150-pound man on the surface of this star would weigh 250,000 tons. He would be crushed under his own weight far more effectively than if he were run over by a steam roller. In fact, even an ant would be smashed to paper thinness at the surface of AC +70° 8247.

According to current ideas a white dwarf is believed to be a star in its final stage of evolution. As a star its life history is over. The only direction it can go is down, as it gradually cools off and settles into extinction as a "black" dwarf.

13 ▶ STAR CLUSTERS

▶ *What are open clusters?*

In an open cluster the number of stars is in the tens and hundreds; there is none of the concentration toward the center that is so characteristic of the globular clusters. Instead, the open clusters have ragged edges with no well-defined shape. Often half a dozen stars will account for as much as half the light of the entire cluster.

▶ *What are globular clusters?*

As the name indicates, these are vast collections of stars arranged in the form of a great sphere or globe. Fig. 92 is a photograph of a typical star cluster in the constellation Hercules called Messier 13. It is 34,000 light years distant. Notice how concentrated the stars are toward the center. Also, that the stars are all of about the same brightness. The globular clusters contain tens to hundreds of thousands of stars. Yet if you lived on a planet revolving around one of the stars near the center you would undoubtedly see more bright stars in the sky than we see, but not nearly so many more as you might think.

▶ *How are globular and open clusters distributed in space?*

Dr. Gerald E. Kron of the Lick Observatory has given an excellent description of the difference in the distribution of the globular and open clusters within our galaxy, the Milky Way system. He remarks that our galaxy is always described as a thin, lens-shaped spiral structure. A person equipped with a pair of spectacles that permitted him to see only the globular clusters

226

would never recognize his own galaxy from this description, for he would see no trace of a lenticular shape or any spiral structure. Instead, he would find globular clusters distributed throughout a vast spherical volume, with only one unusual concentration near the galactic center. Now change glasses to a pair through which our man can see only the open clusters, and what does he find? A structure that has all the earmarks of the familiar flattened spiral. In other words, the globular clusters are grouped roughly in a sphere above and below the galactic plane, while the open clusters are found only along the spiral arms of the Milky Way.

93. The ''Horsehead'' nebula in Orion, a cloud of dark obscuring gas outlined against a light source.

14 ▶ THE LIFE OF A STAR

▶ *Where do the stars come from?*

If astronomers could give a definite answer to this question they would be very happy indeed. At present our ideas on this subject are necessarily vague and speculative. Star formation goes on so slowly that we can never hope to watch a star being born or follow it during its growth and development. But we can look around us in space and see objects which appear to be in different stages of development. The difficulty is in interpreting what we see. Is a red star older than a white one? Are giant stars older than the dwarfs? When a star becomes a nova, what meaning does this have in its life history? These are difficult questions and astronomers do not pretend that they have the final answer. Our ideas on these subjects are changing all the time; some of our cherished present beliefs may be radically changed in a few years, as has happened so many times in the past.

At present, astronomers are of the opinion that stars are born out of the gas and dust that we find along the spiral arms of our galaxy. The gas and dust will not be uniformly distributed but will have knots or condensations in it where matter is more concentrated than usual. These clouds of gas start to contract under the mutual gravitation of their parts. Finally the cloud may form into an opaque mass called a *globule,* which is about a light year in diameter. This contraction generates heat through friction so that the material in the star—which is largely hydrogen—eventually reaches a temperature at which the hydrogen atoms are flying about so fast that they begin to collide with one another and build up helium atoms. In the process of formation of a helium atom, the four hydrogen atoms that make it up lose a little of their mass. This mass that is lost is transformed into radiant energy, according to the well-known formula derived by Einstein some fifty years ago. In this way a globule gradually develops enough heat to become self-luminous and start to shine: A star is born!

▶ Do the stars change?

We know that a star changes rapidly when it becomes a nova and that the sun changes superficially from the increase and decrease of the number of spots on its surface. And we have seen that some stars may expand and contract, as the Cepheid variables do. But do the stars change from one kind to another—from a blue star into a red star, or vice versa?

We believe that the stars *must* change but that these changes are so slow as to be imperceptible during the life of a man, or even in the entire life of civilized man upon the earth. We feel confident today that the source of stellar energy comes from thermonuclear reactions deep in their interior, resulting from the conversion of hydrogen into helium. We find hot blue stars in the dusty regions of the galaxy which must be burning up their hydrogen fuel at a tremendous rate compared with that of the sun. Dr. Allan Sandage of the Mount Wilson and Palomar Observatories has expressed it well in an article on stellar evolution.

"The brightest stars in our galaxy have energy outputs of one hundred thousand times that of the sun. This means that these stars are radiating more rapidly than the sun. They are leading a fast life. Knowing the rate at which stars burn their fuel and knowing the total amount of fuel they have to burn, it is easy to compute how long it takes for all their hydrogen to be consumed. The problem is precisely the same as computing the time at which a furnace will go out if we know the rate it is burning coal and if we know the total amount of coal available to it. The answer turns out that these hot, blue stars found in the dusty regions of galaxies can last for only a few million years. This time is exceedingly short compared with the age of the universe. It is hardly longer than the interval from the present to that time in the past when Homo sapiens climbed down from the trees and walked on two legs. The brightest blue stars of our galaxy are therefore young. This fact, together with the remarkable correlation that wherever we find gas and dust we find these extremely young stars, strongly suggests that cosmic gas and dust is the pre-stellar medium out of which stars are formed." *

* Leaflet No. 308, Astronomical Society of the Pacific, Jan. 1955.

As a star continues to burn up hydrogen in its deep interior, there eventually comes a time when the hydrogen at the center is all converted into helium and the star therefore has a helium core. This helium core disturbs the balance of forces within the star, since helium is four times heavier than hydrogen. Just how the star meets the problem confronting it because of this fact has been the subject of some very difficult mathematical calculations. It appears that the star does so by expanding. As the helium core grows, the star becomes larger and larger. It develops into an enormously inflated object consisting of a relatively small central core at a very high temperature, surrounded by an enormous thin atmosphere. As the star expands, its surface temperature drops and it becomes redder. If a star is massive enough it develops into a red giant like Betelgeuse and Antares, stars with intensely hot cores surrounded by a vast atmosphere at comparatively low surface temperature of 5000° F. It is believed that several billion years may be required for a star slightly more massive than the sun to reach a stage in which the hydrogen in its central core will have been mostly converted into helium. But the changeover to the inflated red giant stage is much more rapid, requiring only some millions of years.

The size of the helium core grows for a time as more hydrogen is consumed at its surface. But all the star is not consumed by the ever-increasing helium core. Current theory has it that only about 12 per cent of the star's material will be used up in this way. The central core may reach a temperature of 200 million degrees Fahrenheit, when new thermonuclear processes may become effective and convert helium into heavier elements. Thus the red giant goes on converting its matter into energy at an ever-increasing pace. But eventually there must come a time when all its sources of nuclear fuel are exhausted. It then begins to contract and for a while its surface becomes hotter and bluer. Ultimately it will decrease in brightness to a point only one millionth of its former luminosity. Like a spendthrift who has exhausted all his sources of credit it has then reached a stage when it is a white dwarf. The star has now no more sources of energy left. All its hydrogen has been burned into helium, and it is so dense that it is impossible for it to contract any more. The only recourse left is for it to cool off slowly, finally becoming an invisible dark body or black dwarf.

231

94. The head of Halley's comet. It has been suggested that Halley's comet might have been the Star of Bethlehem.

15 ▶ WHAT WAS THE STAR OF BETHLEHEM?

▶ *What was the star of Bethlehem?*

At Christmastime astronomers are often asked, "What was the star of Bethlehem?"

About all an astronomer can do is shake his head regretfully, say that no such star as the star of Bethlehem now exists, and that there is no scientific evidence of its existence at any time. But he might also cautiously admit that there are a few ways in which the appearance of such a remarkable object as the star of Bethlehem might be explained. "For example, suppose that we assume—" and he proceeds to discuss some of the things that might have happened. Let us follow his discussion and see what some of these possibilities are.

It is related that the Magi had seen a star in the east which heralded the birth of a King of the Jews. They traveled to Jerusalem, told Herod of the star, and wished to know where He was that they might worship Him. Herod sent them to Bethlehem because it had been prophesied that the Messiah would be born in the city of David.

"When they had heard the king they departed; and, lo, the star, which they saw in the east, went before them, till it came and stood where the young child was.

"When they saw the star they rejoiced with exceeding great joy."

The Magi worshiped the child and gave Him gifts, and then, warned that Herod sought to destroy Him, went by another way to their own country.

There is no other mention of the star in the scriptures or in other historical accounts.

In seeking a rational explanation, it must be remembered that the Chaldeans were assiduous observers of the heavens, so that the positions of the fixed stars and the motions of the planets were a familiar story to them. Indeed, there is every reason to believe that the ancients were much better acquainted with the constellations than are the people of today, who can seldom get a good look at the night sky because of artificial illumination. The Chaldeans would never make the obvious blunder of mistaking a bright star such as Sirius for the sign for which they were waiting, or even one of the bright planets, Mars, Jupiter, or Venus. We must look for something very unusual in the sky, some exceptional and awe-inspiring event that occurred about the time of the birth of Christ.

Here we get into trouble at once, for history is so vague and confusing on this point that it is impossible to fix the birth with any certainty, but it is probable that 5 B.C. would not be greatly in error. (Many people may ask what is the matter with December 25, in the year A.D. 1. Our use of the year of the birth of Jesus as the era from which to reckon time came from a suggestion by the learned Roman monk Dionysius Exiguus, who died in A.D. 556. He computed the date of the birth to be 754 A.U.C. [from the founding of Rome] and although this is now known to be wrong, the system has become so firmly established that nothing can now be done about it. Thus we have the anachronism that Jesus was born sometime in the period that is called Before Christ. And the actual month and day is even more hopelessly obscure, for December 25 was not celebrated as Christmas until the fourth century, long after the real date was forgotten.)

A possibility that has received serious consideration is that the star of Bethlehem was produced by two planets coming so close together that to weak eyes their light might have seemed to come from a single star. In astronomical language, they were in conjunction. If it could be shown that an unusually close conjunction occurred at about the right time, the coincidence would be very striking, to say the least. Several attempts have been made to establish the date of the true Annus Domini by this means.

Now when the positions of the planets are traced back to the time of Christ, it is found that Jupiter and Saturn were in conjunction three times in the year 7 B.C. This discovery was made over a century ago by the German chronologist C. L. Ideler. According to him, the first conjunction would appear as the sign for which the Magi had been waiting, and would have started them on their journey to Jerusalem. The last conjunction was so close that the two planets might have appeared merged into one, and would also have been in the proper position in the sky to have led the Magi from Jerusalem to Bethlehem. Ideler believed that these conjunctions satisfied the conditions regarding the star of Bethlehem so well that they established the time of the birth of Christ as 7 B.C.

In 1856 the Rev. Charles Pritchard, a clergyman and professor of astronomy who did important work on the distances of the stars, made a careful check on Ideler's conclusions, and as a result found that while there were three conjunctions of Jupiter and Saturn in 7 B.C., they did not occur at the times given by Ideler. He found also that the two planets were never closer than twice the diameter of the full moon, and so could not possibly have been mistaken for one. The Rev. Mr. Pritchard's calculations were confirmed independently by the Greenwich Observatory, and there seems to be no reason to doubt their correctness. Thus the hypothesis of a close conjunction, although ingenious, is capable of being mathematically tested and is found definitely wrong.

Let us now consider an entirely different type of object that might explain the star but which, at best, can only be regarded as a reasonable guess.

One may scan the heavens for years and never see anything that has not been seen before. But tomorrow night an amateur astronomer looking at the Milky Way may see a star as bright as Venus blazing there where no star of that size has any right to be. Such new stars are called novae (see p. 211), and although they seldom become this conspicuous, there are a few that have attained great brilliance. The brightest on record appeared in 1572 and was more brilliant than Venus. Another in 1604 was almost as bright. Both were carefully studied, the first by the Danish astronomer Tycho Brahé and the second by his pupil Kepler. The next brightest novae were in 1901, 1918, and 1942.

A nova may maintain its extraordinary brilliance for a few days; but then it begins to fade, and although there may be minor flare-ups, it never regains its original brightness. Finally, it sinks into obscurity again, a "morning glory" that has had its brief moment of public acclaim.

It is, of course, impossible to say whether or not the star of

235

Bethlehem was a nova, but there are several reasons why such a supposition seems fairly plausible. In the first place, a nova would easily account for the great brilliance of the star. Second, a new star of this kind would be regarded as a sign of supernatural origin that could not fail to be heeded by everyone. Finally, the nova would have remained conspicuous long enough for the Magi to have completed their journey before it faded from sight, which would explain why it was never mentioned later. Against the idea of a nova is the fact that there is no independent record of a bright new star having been observed by other people, such as the Chinese or Japanese. It seems impossible that they could have missed such a spectacular object.

Still another explanation that remains to be considered makes a stronger appeal to the imagination than any of those already mentioned. There is just a little evidence that the star of Bethlehem might have been Halley's comet.

An extensive search of old chronicles reveals the definite record of a comet at the proper season and in the right part of the sky for every one of the twenty-seven times that Halley's comet has visited the earth between 87 B.C. and A.D. 1910. One of the earliest, and at the same time one of the most certain, returns of the comet was in 11 B.C. As stated before, the date of the birth of Christ is not known, except that it was probably about 5 B.C. Although this is six years after the appearance of the comet, history is so indefinite that the interval does not seem overly long. A bright comet could not fail to arouse universal wonder and excitement, as a sign heralding the arrival of the new King.

But there is another scrap of evidence that makes the visit of 11 B.C. of peculiar interest. During the latter part of August of that year, it is recorded that Halley's comet was in the constellation of Gemini, the twins, a little north of the two bright stars Castor and Pollux. The latitude of Bethlehem is 31 degrees 42 minutes, and it so happens that 2000 years ago Castor and Pollux were almost exactly 31 degrees 42 minutes north of what astronomers call the celestial equator. This means that Castor and Pollux, in their daily journey across the celestial sphere, passed through the zenith of Bethlehem. And since Halley's comet came very close to Castor and Pollux, it must also at one time have stood directly over Bethlehem—"the place where the young child was."

Thus astronomers can scarcely be accused of making no effort to solve the problem, for they have at least investigated the possibility of a celestial object having been directly over Bethlehem, at about the time historians give for the birth of Christ. Just how it could have pointed out the right dwelling to the Magi is still a mystery, but perhaps it is better that some of the questions remain unanswered. The story has endured for two thousand years because of its beauty and simplicity.

16 ▶ GREATER AGGREGATIONS OF STARS—THE GALAXIES

▶ *What is the shape of our galaxy?*

Just a casual glance at the night sky is enough to show that the stars are not distributed over it at random but occur most often in a bright band called the Milky Way. The bright stars are indeed scattered somewhat irregularly over the sky, but as we go to the more numerous, fainter stars we find them concentrated near the Milky Way. Of the stars that can be observed with a large telescope, it has been estimated that about forty times as many are found in the Milky Way as at points far distant from it. Even with a small telescope turned upon the Milky Way we find that this band of light is thickly powdered with stars, and if we take a photograph of it the stars crowd upon one another so closely that there seems to be no end to them. We certainly get the impression very strongly that when we look into the Milky Way we are looking through a great depth or thickness of stars, while when we look away from it the stars are spread much more thinly in space.

Such an idea was clearly stated by Sir William Herschel a century and a half ago when he proposed his famous "grindstone" theory of the Milky Way structure. He did this by his method of star gauges, counting the stars in various directions in space, beginning at the Milky Way and working out away from it. In this manner he found that the stars are not at all equally distributed throughout space but are much more numerous as we approach the Milky Way. He interpreted this as meaning that near the Milky Way we are looking through a greater depth of stars, while in regions where stars are scarce we see only the comparatively few in our line of sight.

This led him to the view that the stars are not arranged in space in the form of a sphere at equal distances throughout, but in the form of a flattened disk whose diameter is about ten times its thickness. Herschel's general view of the Milky Way has been confirmed and worked out in more detail by modern observations. If our Milky Way or galaxy of stars could be seen from the outside it would probably bear a resemblance to some of the spiral nebulae shown on photographs taken with giant telescopes. The sun with its attendant planets is now believed to lie at a point about halfway outward from the center to the edge of the stellar system. We are, however, near the central plane of the galactic system. That is the reason the Milky Way extends in a great band entirely around the sky, and as we look to greater distances away from the central plane fewer stars are found outside the boundaries of the Milky Way.

▶ *What is the form of our stellar system?*

We believe that our stellar system has the shape of a discus, as shown in Fig. 95. In the center is a huge nucleus of stars which contains most of the mass of the system. Winding out from the central nucleus are the spiral arms of the galaxy. The whole forms in space a lens-shaped figure, bulged at the center and flattened outward toward the edges. The system is probably over 100,000 light years in diameter and perhaps 20,000 light years thick. It is now known to be in rotation around the central bulge which lies in the direction of the constellation Sagittarius. The sun is on the upper or north side of the central plane, about 30,000 light years distant from the galactic center. It is not far from the center of a collection of some millions of stars, known as the local system or cluster, which apparently is a secondary unit of the larger system. The sun makes one revolution about the galactic center in about 200 million years, traveling at the rate of 180 miles per second. The total number of stars in our galaxy is estimated to be of the order of one hundred billion. Overlying the galaxy on either side like an atmosphere is a thin layer of stars that form what is called the halo.

Far above and below the galactic plane are great groups of stars arranged in the closely packed spherical forms of the globular

239

clusters. They are at immense distances, the nearest being some ten thousand light years from the sun. It was the arrangement of these globular clusters in the sky that gave us our first clue that the sun is situated far to one side of the central galactic bulge. Though globular clusters are scattered all around the sky, nearly half of them are located in the regions of the constellations of Ophiuchus, Sagittarius, and Scorpio. Their concentration in this region was an early indication that this was the direction of the center of our galaxy, which we now believe is about 30,000 light years away from the sun. Some globular clusters are found at distances as great as 75,000 light years from the plane of the Milky Way.

▶ *Is our galaxy rotating?*

The appearance of many of the nebulae that show spiral structure suggests that they are rotating. If our galaxy has the same general shape we assume it must be rotating too. There are two ways in which it might rotate. It might rotate as a solid body like the wheel of a car. If this were the case, the relative positions of all the particles in the wheel are fixed with relation

95. Our galactic system is believed to consist of a flattened aggregation of stars in the form of a discus. Here we see it edge-on. The large white spots are the globular clusters. The sun is a little more than halfway from center to edge.

to one another, so that it would be impossible to detect any motion within the system. In the second case we assume that the galaxy is not rotating as a solid body, but that the matter within it is revolving around the central bulge of stars where most of the mass is situated, in the same way that the planets revolve around the sun. In this case, the stars nearest the central bulge revolve the fastest, and the velocity decreases as we go outward toward the rim. The particles that compose the rings of Saturn revolve in the same way, each particle moving in a separate orbit of its own, depending upon its distance from Saturn. Observations show that the stars in our galaxy are revolving as in this second case, like the particles in the rings of Saturn. Each star in the galaxy is moving around the central bulge in an orbit of its own, at a speed depending upon its distance from the center, only these orbits are vast beyond comparison with those of the planets.

From observations of stars so distant that they do not share the motion of the sun it has been possible to find how rapidly the sun is moving around the center of our galaxy. The speed of the sun in its orbit is 180 miles per second, and its period of revolution 200 million years. During the whole of the earth's existence it has probably not had time to make more than ten complete circuits. It is assumed that the sun is moving in a circular orbit about the galactic center, and the particular direction toward which we are headed at present is the constellation of Cygnus. The sun also has a slight motion of its own in relation to the stars close around it, like the motion of an individual bird among the members of a flock. Relative to these stars the sun is moving at the rate of 12 miles per second toward the constellation of Hercules. You might say that the sun is on a grand tour of the galaxy which will take it completely around in 200 million years. But it is also engaged in a local side trip in the direction of Hercules.

▶ *What are "galaxies"?*

We have seen that the great nebula in Andromeda appears to the unaided eye as a hazy patch of light about the size of the full moon. When it is photographed with a powerful telescope, however, it appears as an oval mass of light with a

241

pronounced central condensation surrounded by spiral arms. On the best photographs we can easily see that the outer parts of the spiral arms are resolved into stars but we cannot be sure about the central condensation, whether it consists of stars, dust, or what. We can photograph other objects in the sky that generally resemble the Andromeda nebula, although they differ in details and the way they are turned toward us. Some appear with the spiral arms more tightly wound than in Andromeda. In others the arms are spread farther apart. Some are turned toward us edge-on, so that the spiral arms are hidden. Others we see broadside so that the spiral structure is clearly revealed. These galaxies remind us of vast cosmic pinwheels. Other galaxies do not show spiral structure but resemble spindles or oval balls of light, depending upon our angle of view. Still others appear as irregular cloudy masses, as do the Magellanic Clouds.

Before about 1920 our ideas of the nature of these objects were so different from our present conception as to be hardly recognizable now. We were uncertain as to whether they were glowing clouds of gas—like the nebula in Orion—or whether they were vast stellar systems clear outside our Milky Way system. Because both types of objects are superficially similar in appearance, they were all called *nebulae,* a word meaning "clouds." Now we know that they are two entirely different types of object, as different as stars and shooting stars. Today the clouds of gas and dust within the Milky Way are properly referred to as nebulae. But the objects outside our Milky Way are called galaxies. We know that these are immense aggregations of stars similar to our Milky Way system but situated far outside it, at distances (except in a few isolated cases) of many millions of light years.

▶ *How do we know the distances of the galaxies?*

The distance of the nearer galaxies, such as the one in Andromeda, has been measured by the stars they contain. We

96. Whirlpool galaxy in constellation of Canes Venatici. This is a galaxy seen face-on. It is possible our galaxy may resemble this system.

have seen that if we know the absolute magnitude of a star—its magnitude at a distance of 10 parsecs or 32.6 light years—and also its apparent magnitude, then we can calculate its distance immediately. (If we know that a 100-watt light has a certain brightness at a distance of a mile, and if it looks one fourth this bright, then we know it must be two miles away, since the intensity of light changes in inverse proportion to the square of the distance.) In 1917 two novae (new stars) appeared in the Andromeda galaxy; they showed as faint stars on the photographs. Since novae at maximum brilliance are very bright stars, this indicated the Andromeda galaxy could not be in the Milky Way—otherwise the novae would have appeared much brighter. Also, it looked as if the edges of the Andromeda galaxy consisted of stars instead of being gaseous. Even so, stars had been found in the gaseous nebulae and independent proof of their distance was desirable.

This was obtained from a study of some of the individual stars in the Andromeda galaxy which were found to be Cepheid variables. As we have already seen, there is a definite relation between the period of light variation and the absolute luminosity of the Cepheids, in which the longer the period the brighter the star. Thus Cepheids can be used as distance indicators. By 1929 forty Cepheids had been identified, with periods ranging from 10 to 48 days. Referring to the period–luminosity curve for the Lesser Magellanic Cloud, the corresponding absolute magnitude for stars of this period could be obtained. Then, knowing their apparent magnitudes the distance to the Andromeda galaxy could be found quickly. The distance determined in 1929 was 900,000 light years. Later, when this was corrected to compensate for obscuring matter in space the figure was reduced to 750,000 light years. Now that the distance of the galaxy was known, its size could be found. It appeared that our Milky Way system was much larger than the Andromeda galaxy but that the difference in size was not greater than that found among other galaxies.

97. In about 1900, astronomers did not know whether the nebulae were glowing masses of gas in our Milky Way, like the North American nebula or universes of stars.

The distance of 750,000 light years to the Andromeda galaxy was generally accepted until 1952, when the first photographs of this object taken with the 200-inch telescope indicated something was wrong. It had confidently been expected that the 200-inch would reveal a certain type of star called RR Lyrae or cluster variables which were too faint to show on photographs taken with the 100-inch telescope, but from all indications should be just within the reach of the 200-inch. Yet these stars failed to show. This meant that either the cluster variables were *fainter* than had been supposed, or that the Andromeda galaxy was *farther away*. But the luminosity of the cluster-type variables could be checked with other stars of known luminosity and was found to be all right. It therefore seemed probable that the Andromeda galaxy was farther away than had been supposed, and that the absolute magnitude of the Cepheids used in fixing the "zero point" on the period–luminosity curve was in error. On the basis of the stars that could be resolved with the 200-inch telescope it appeared that the Cepheids were 1.5 magnitudes brighter than indicated by the accepted period–luminosity relation. As a result of this, the currently accepted value for the distance of the Andromeda galaxy had to be multiplied by two. This meant that the distance of the Andromeda galaxy is 1,500,000 light years instead of 750,000 light years as had been supposed. Later it was moved out again to a little more than 2 million light years.

▶ *Why is determining the distance of the Andromeda galaxy so important?*

The Andromeda galaxy has been used as a measuring stick for determining the distances to other galaxies. We observe some of the brightest objects in the Andromeda galaxy—novae, globular star clusters, and so on—and obtain their absolute brightness from their known distance. Then we search for these same objects in other, more distant galaxies. By observing their apparent

98. The great galaxy in Andromeda at a distance of 2,000,000 light years from the earth. This object appears as a hazy patch of light on a dark night. It is the farthest that you can see.

magnitudes we can reverse the process and find their distances also. For the more remote galaxies that show no stars or globular clusters, distance has to be based upon their magnitude as a whole. These magnitudes are then compared with the total luminosity of those whose distances are known. Thus it is seen that the distances assigned to all the galaxies depend very critically upon the ac-

99. Different types of galaxies.

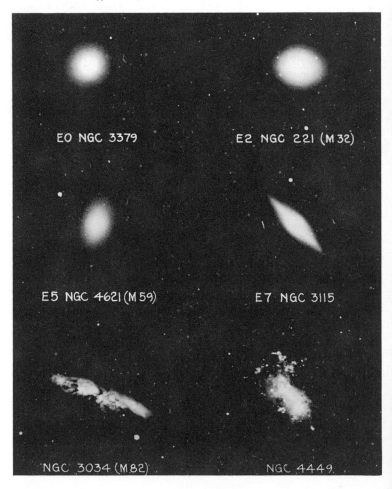

curate distance measurement of the Andromeda galaxy and a few other close spirals.

At present our ideas of distance are still in a state of flux so that the distance of about 2,000,000 light years to the Andromeda galaxy given here should not be regarded as final. All our present distance indicators (such as the Cepheids) are now being checked. It will still be some time before we can speak with confidence of distances outside the Milky Way.

▶ What is the farthest we can see?

Ask this question at a party sometime. It will catch people entirely unawares. Most people have no idea of the distance they can see into space. Probably they will first think of how far they can see on the earth, which of course is only a few miles. Then they will remember immediately that they can see the moon, which is obviously at a much greater distance—as we have seen, about 239,000 miles. But as celestial distances go, the moon is practically in our back yard. Of course we can see much farther into space than this. In the solar system the faintest object we can see is the planet Uranus, which is barely on the limit of visibility to the naked eye. It is at a distance of 1,785 million miles. But again we are not looking any distance into space at all, for the stars are immeasurably farther away than any object in the solar system. Even the nearest star—Alpha Centauri—is 25 trillion miles or 4.3 light years distant. And Alpha Centauri is the third brightest star in the sky.

In the southern hemisphere you can see two objects which look like a part of the Milky Way that had gotten separated from the main band. These are the Magellanic Clouds, which are not really clouds at all but aggregations of millions of stars. Their distance is estimated at 150,000 light years. The Magellanic Clouds are bright objects in the sky, so we can easily see to this distance.

If you look at the constellation of Andromeda on a clear, moonless night—about halfway between Cassiopeia and the northeast corner of the Square of Pegasus—you should be able to catch a glimpse of a hazy patch of light about the size of the full moon. This is usually referred to as the great galaxy in Andromeda. It is a collection of stars similar to our Milky Way system and larger

249

than the Magellanic Clouds. We do not feel so confident about the exact distance of the Andromeda galaxy as we did a decade or so ago, but at the present time astronomers put its distance at a little more than 2,000,000 light years away. As we have seen, before 1952 astronomers thought the distance to the Andromeda galaxy was 750,000 light years, but when certain kinds of stars of absolute magnitude 0.0 failed to show on the early photographs of the Andromeda galaxy taken with the 200-inch telescope, they realized that something must be wrong with their distance scale. To adjust matters they decided that the universe outside our own Milky Way system must be twice as large as had been supposed. So the distance to the Andromeda galaxy and others was doubled at one stroke.

The Andromeda galaxy, then, is the farthest object we can see without telescopic aid. Perhaps some primitive man turning his eyes toward the heavens caught a momentary glimpse of this object and wondered about it. Why did it appear as a patch of light instead of a point of light like the stars? What a long way we have had to come before we could furnish the beginning of an answer to that question!

▶ *How has intergalactic dust hindered the exploration of space?*

One of the most serious obstacles to galactic exploration until recently was the difficulty of penetrating very far into space due to obscuration and dimming of starlight by interstellar dust. This interstellar dust is very thin, judged by ordinary standards. There are perhaps 16 hydrogen atoms per cubic inch, while the number of small solid grains is much smaller, about 100 in a cubic mile. But we look through such a tremendous depth of obscuring matter that it adds up finally to a real obstacle, thin as it is. The effect of this dust in space is to redden starlight in somewhat the same way that the particles in our atmosphere redden

100. A spiral galaxy seen edge-on through foreground stars in our Milky Way. Note dark obscuring matter across galactic nucleus.

the light of the sun near the horizon. Only the particles in space are not so good at reddening starlight as our atmosphere. Thirty years ago one of the things that used to puzzle astronomers was the fact that some very luminous O and B stars were redder than they should be. Astronomers knew from the lines in their spectrum that these must be very hot, bright stars. Yet instead of being white they were yellowish. Now we know it is because we see these excessively luminous stars at great distances, which means that their light is shining through vast stretches of cosmic dust, so that by the time the beam reaches us a considerable amount of space-reddening exists.

Red light is not scattered so much by fine dust particles as blue light is, which means that red is much more penetrating than blue light. A photograph of a distant landscape taken in blue light may show only a blank wall of haze, while the same scene photographed in red light penetrates the haze and shows the details of the landscape beyond. We can apply the same principle to photographing objects in our galaxy. Photographs taken in blue light penetrate only a short distance into space before the light is stopped by scattering from interstellar dust. But photographs taken in red and infrared light penetrate to much greater distances. By means of photographs taken on extremely fast red-sensitive plates it has been possible to penetrate most if not all of the cosmic haze that obscures the central portion of our galaxy.

▶ *How have radio waves helped in the exploration of the galaxy?*

In some parts of the Milky Way we find great dark places silhouetted against the background of a distant starfield. Astronomers used to think that these dark rifts might be holes in the sky where they could see into the depths of space beyond. Now they know that these are clouds of dust that completely block out the light of the stars beyond them. The few stars visible in the dark

101. A spiral nebula of the barred type in the constellation of Eridanus.

252

regions are foreground stars, between us and the cosmic dust cloud. Recently an entirely new method of penetrating the dust clouds of space has been discovered, far more powerful than even the red and infrared light used in photography. This is by means of light of vastly longer wavelength than red or infrared light. The light

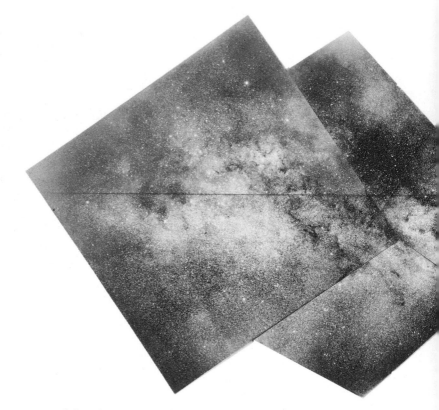

used in photography has a wavelength of about 0.00003 inches. But the wavelength of the radiation used in this new method of exploring the galaxy is in the radio region with a wavelength of 8 inches. It is a form of radiation that is produced very rarely by hydrogen atoms in the cold of space. In fact, it is only once in

254

102. A mosaic map of the Milky Way showing star clouds and dark obscuring dust clouds.

every 100 million years on the average that a hydrogen atom emits radiation of this wavelength. We would never be able to detect it if we were not gazing through such vast depths of space with so many hydrogen atoms in our line of sight. That radiation of this wavelength should be emitted by hydrogen gas was predicted theoretically by a young Dutch astrophysicist, H. van de Hulst, in 1944, and the radiation was actually detected observationally in 1951. These radio waves penetrate right through the galaxy in most directions. Thus by radio exploration we are able to explore the structure of the galaxy in a way that is impossible with optical telescopes that depend on visible or near-visible light.

▶ What is the "red shift?"

Back in 1914, Dr. V. M. Slipher of the Lowell Observatory at Flagstaff, Arizona, began a program of photographing the spectra of the galaxies or universes of stars outside our Milky Way system, such as the Andromeda galaxy and others. The work went slowly because he did not have a large telescope at his command and the galaxies are faint, diffuse objects hard to register satisfactorily on a photographic plate. Slipher continued this work until 1925, when the spectra of forty-five galaxies had been obtained.

The principal thing Slipher was interested in was the velocities of these galaxies toward or away from the earth. It will be remembered that astronomers can figure this velocity from the Doppler shift of the spectrum lines from their normal position toward red or violet, a shift toward the red indicating a velocity away from the earth and a shift toward the violet a velocity of approach. The first velocities of the brighter galaxies such as the one in Andromeda gave a velocity of approach of 190 miles per second. But as he went to fainter and presumably more distant galaxies, velocities indicating motion away from the earth were

103. Irregular nebula in Cygnus showing dust clouds of obscuring matter.

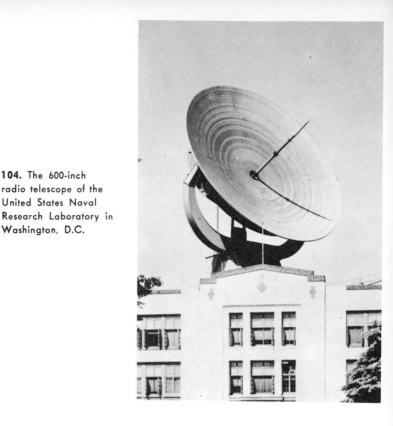

104. The 600-inch radio telescope of the United States Naval Research Laboratory in Washington, D.C.

found in increasing numbers until they completely dominated the list. There is no reason we can see why more galaxies should be going away from the earth than should be coming toward us. After all, the earth is not at any particularly favored position in space with relation to these distant objects. So we should expect their motions to be entirely at random, as many approaching as receding. But it was quite obvious that their motions, so far as the earth was concerned, were *not* at random. Many more were receding than approaching. Also, in general, the fainter the galaxy the faster its velocity of recession.

By 1925 Slipher had gone as far as he could with the telescopic equipment available to him. About this time the work was taken up by Hubble and Humason at the Mount Wilson Observatory,

258

using the 100-inch telescope, then the largest in existence. Within a few years they were able to obtain the spectra of much fainter objects than had been possible before. In every case the spectra showed a shift toward the red, indicating a velocity of recession. Moreover, it was found that this speed of recession depended directly upon the distance of the galaxy. In other words, the more distant a galaxy the faster it appeared to be rushing away from us. This is called the law of the red shift. According to present estimates of the distance of the galaxies, the red shift indicates a velocity of recession of 40 miles per second for every million light years of distance.

The spectrum lines measured are two in the violet, just within the sensitivity range of the eye, known as Fraunhofer's H and K lines, produced by calcium atoms, having a wavelength of 3934 and 3968 Angstrom units. (An Angstrom unit is 250 millionths of an inch.) Let us see how much of a red shift we get for a star moving along at the fairly swift clip of 100 miles per second. It is a simple matter to do this. We divide this velocity by the velocity of light (186,000 miles per second), and multiply by the normal wavelength of the light when at rest. For a velocity of 100 miles per second we find that we should get a displacement toward the red of about 2 Angstrom units. But in the most distant galaxies whose spectra have been photographed we get a red shift amounting to around 800 Angstrom units. The H and K lines are shifted out of the violet part of the spectrum into the blue-green region. This corresponds to galaxies in the cluster in the constellation of Hydra at a distance of one billion light years. Such large red shifts have made their photography more difficult, for instead of using plates with a violet-sensitive emulsion astronomers have been forced to use slower panchromatic plates that are sensitive to blue-green light.

▶ *What is meant by "the expanding universe"?*

The red shift indicates that everything outside our local group of galaxies is rushing from us faster and faster the farther away it is. (The galaxies in the local group are so "near" that the red shift for them is smaller than the spectrum shift produced by their own individual motions. For example, the red shift

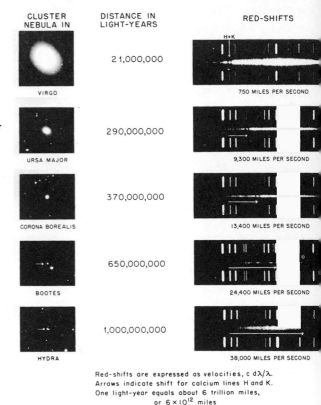

105. The red shift for galaxies at different distances.

CLUSTER NEBULA IN	DISTANCE IN LIGHT-YEARS	RED-SHIFTS
VIRGO	2 1,000,000	750 MILES PER SECOND
URSA MAJOR	290,000,000	9,300 MILES PER SECOND
CORONA BOREALIS	370,000,000	13,400 MILES PER SECOND
BOOTES	650,000,000	24,400 MILES PER SECOND
HYDRA	1,000,000,000	38,000 MILES PER SECOND

Red-shifts are expressed as velocities, c dλ/λ.
Arrows indicate shift for calcium lines H and K.
One light-year equals about 6 trillion miles,
or 6×10^{12} miles

for the Andromeda galaxy at a distance of perhaps two million light years amounts to less than 2 Angstrom units.) Thus everywhere we look in space objects appear to be moving outward. Now, there is no reason why all these objects should be flying away from *us*. There can hardly be any special significance to *our* particular position in space. It must be because the *whole universe* is expanding. If that is the case, then regardless of where we were

260

located in it all the objects around us would appear to be moving away from us. The situation is often compared to the seeds inside a growing watermelon. If you measured the distance from any particular seed to those around it they would all appear to be moving away, and the more distant seeds would be moving the fastest.

If the universe is expanding as observations indicate, getting bigger as time goes on, then if we ran time backward the universe would get smaller until finally at some remote epoch all the material in it must have been concentrated into one gigantic primeval atom. Then "something" happened; there was a terrific explosion, and matter started rushing outward in all directions (an idea described by its opponents as the "big bang" hypothesis.) And since there was nothing to stop it, the matter has gone on exploding ever since.

According to another hypothesis the universe may not go on expanding indefinitely but may be alternately expanding and contracting—pulsating, in other words—so that the universe might contract to its former superdense state and explode all over again. Which would mean that some 15 billion years hence we might find ourselves doing everything all over again. According to still another idea, the universe is expanding but has always been in its present state and will always remain so. This is called the "steady state" theory of the universe. We ask immediately: If the universe is expanding, how can it remain in its present state? It must certainly begin to thin out after a while. But no—according to this idea there was never a time when the universe was contracted into a single hard knot, and there will never be a time when it has expanded until it is infinitely rarified. The universe never had any beginning and it has no end. Space as well as time is infinite. And as space expands, matter is created at just the right rate to keep the average-amount-per-unit volume the same. The quantity created is small in ordinary terms. It amounts to the creation of one hydrogen atom in a large room about once every thousand years. The situation might be likened to the way the government prints new bank notes to keep up with the expanding population. As the population increases the printing presses keep turning out more paper money so that the amount per person remains steady. At present there is no clear-cut observational test that can be made

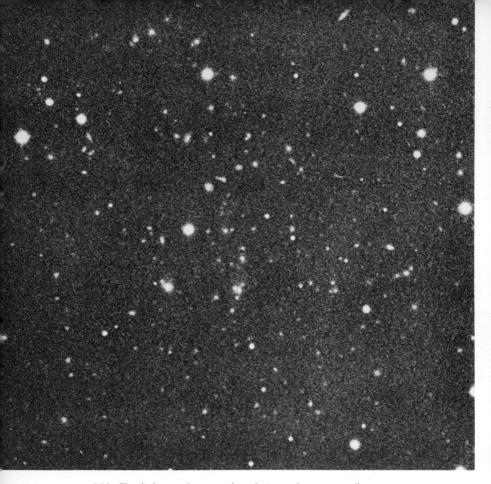

106. The little smudges on this photograph are actually galaxies, like that in Andromeda at a distance estimated to be a billion light years.

which will tell us which theory is right and which is wrong. (Of course it could be that they are *all* wrong!) All we can do is to continue to observe the universe with every means at our command in the hope that we will uncover clues which will give us the answer to the questions that perplex us now.

17 ▶ A LOOK AT THE CONSTELLATIONS

▶ *Why don't the constellations resemble the objects after which they are named?*

When we look at the stars we see them arranged in the form of geometrical figures—lines, semicircles, triangles, squares. But we know that ancient people named these groups of stars after their gods and goddesses and familiar animals. Yet we can't find anything in the sky that bears the remotest resemblance to a dog or a sea monster or a giant. What was the matter with these people? How could they see things in the sky which are certainly not apparent to us today?

The answer is that they couldn't see the figures of persons and animals formed by the outline of the stars any better than we can. And we mustn't expect that they did. Today we name a lot of things after people and animals, but not because they look like them. For example, the state of Washington on the map does not look like George Washington. The peak in southern California on which the 100-inch telescope is located is called Mount Wilson, named after the first mayor of Los Angeles, but it doesn't look in the least like Mayor Wilson. There is a lake in Canada called Great Bear Lake but it doesn't look like a bear. Nobody expects these objects to resemble the people and animals after which they are named. Just so you must not expect the constellations to look like the people and animals after which *they* are named. They were given these names so long ago that their origin is hopelessly lost, just as several thousand years hence people will wonder how some of our names originated.

▶ *How important are the constellations in astronomy?*

Here we are going to tell you something that you will probably never see in any other star book. The study of the constellations is of no special importance in *astronomy*. The study of the constellations properly belongs to mythology, and only in an incidental way has any connection with the science of astronomy. This is hard for many people to realize, since there is often so much emphasis put in popular books on astronomy on learning the names of the stars and the constellations. It may therefore come as a surprise to hear that many of the foremost astronomers hardly know the constellations at all except for a few, like the Big Dipper, that everybody knows. But if you will think about it for a moment, you will see that merely knowing the *name* that the ancients gave to a star or group of stars tells nothing about the stars themselves. For example, suppose you know that Aldebaran is a red star that marks the right eye of the bull in the constellation Taurus. You can identify it in the sky but you still know nothing about Aldebaran as a *star,* as a *physical body.* It is like meeting Mr. John Green for the first time. Just knowing his name tells you nothing about Mr. John Green as a personality. Is he generous and easy-going or stingy and irritable? You have to know Mr. Green a while and study him before you can begin to understand him as a person. Similarly, if you want to know about the stars you will have to go deeper than merely being able to identify them by name in the sky.

▶ *Is there any use, then, in learning the constellations?*

Yes, we think there is or we would not have included a set of star maps in this book. For some reason people like the constellations and there is no doubt that they are going to stay there in the sky. After you get to know them they seem like old friends. Also they serve as convenient landmarks for quick reference purposes to different regions of the sky. Thus if you wanted to tell a friend where to look for a new comet you might say that it is in the center of the great square of Pegasus moving northeast into Andromeda. If a new star blazes up in the sky it is identified by the constellation in which it appears, such as Nova Puppis, Nova Auriga, or Nova Herculis. Also, astronomers designate the stars by the letters of the Greek alphabet according to their brightness and depending upon the constellation in which they occur. Vega, for example, is the brightest star in the constellation of Lyra and is referred to as Alpha (α) Lyrae; the second brightest star is Beta (β) Lyrae; the third brightest Gamma (γ) Lyrae, and so on. (The genetive or possessive case is always used.) If it is a bright star besides having a proper name, it may also be referred to as number such-and-such in somebody's star catalogue. A bright star may thus have a dozen aliases.

▶ What is the best way to learn the constellations?

The best way to learn the constellations is to get somebody who already knows them to point them out to you. This is almost too easy and perhaps not so much fun as learning them yourself. Still it must be admitted that the stars look very bewildering when you first try to become acquainted with them, and it is certainly a great help to have an experienced person around to get you oriented in the sky.

If you can't get help, the best course is to start with a constellation that is so well marked you cannot fail to recognize it. By far the easiest constellation to identify are the seven stars that form part of the constellation of the Great Bear, what we ordinarily call the Big Dipper. Hold Map 1 so that the stars which form its outline appear in the same position as those in the sky. Now fix your attention upon the two in the end of the bowl of the Big Dipper, called the Pointers. A line drawn through the Pointers passes through a star of about the same brightness which is our north star, or Polaris. Polaris is at the end of the handle of the Little Dipper or the tail of the Little Bear. The stars that form the Little Dipper are not so bright as those in the Big Dipper but still you should have no trouble in locating them.

Now that you have found the Big Dipper and Little Dipper you can work outward from them. For example, you should have no trouble in locating Cassiopeia, since it is on the opposite side of the pole from the Big Dipper and about the same distance from it. Cassiopeia is easily recognized from the five stars in it that form a rather straggly-looking W. Constellations near Cassiopeia which are not so well marked are Perseus, Andromeda, and Cepheus.

In the beginning it is best to try to identify constellations that contain bright stars which are easily recognized such as Orion, Canis Major, Scorpio, Taurus, and Aquila, to mention only a few. Once you have identified these it is fairly easy to pick out the less conspicuous ones. And if you find yourself unable to identify them you have this consolation. A lot of professional astronomers can't either.

▶ INDEX

267

268

270

Moon, 16, 18, 49, 108
  atmosphere of, 46-49
  changing appearance of, 34-35
  comets and, 175
  craters on, 38-39, 45, 49-56
  distance from earth, 30-31, 56-57, 114
  eclipses of, 63-64
  liberations of, 40
  maria on, 35, 43, 45-46
  markings on, 35
  movement of, in relation to earth, 41-42
    in relation to sun, 42-43
  orbit of, 57, 63
  revolutions of, 39
  rising and setting of, 32-33
  rotation of, 38-40
  size and weight of, 31-32
  and tides, 192
  time needed for rocket to reach, 57-59
  volcanos on, 38
Moonlight, 36
Moons (see Satellites)
Moore, J. H., 148
Motion-picture photography, 86-87
Mount Wilson, 4, 24, 134
Murray, Margaret Lindsay, Lady Huggins, 13

Naval Observatory, 130-131
Nebulae, 15, 17, 242
Nebular hypothesis, 190-193
Neptune (planet), 49, 74, 102, 108, 114
  distance from sun, 153
  satellite of, 108, 149
  speed of, 178
New moon, 36-37, 42-43
Newcomb, Simon, 56
Newton, Isaac, 69-70, 107
Nicholson, Seth B., 149, 157-159
19 Piscium (star), 202
Nitrogen, 97
  on Mars, 125
Northern lights, 91
Novae, 211, 235-236, 244
  identification of, 264-265
Nuclear reactions, 96-97

Observatories, 1, 3-9
  (See also name of observatory, as Mount Wilson)

Oceanus Procellarum, 45
Omega Centauri (star cluster), 219
Omicron Cete (star), 101
Omicron Herculis (star), 210
Ophiuchus, constellation of, 240
Orbits, 191
  of asteroids, 155, 157-159
  of comets, 169
  of Encke's comet, 176-177
  of Mars, 191
  of Mercury, 176, 191
  of moon, 57, 63
  of planets, 155
  of stars, 204-205
Orion, constellation of, 185, 266
  nebula in, 242
Oxygen, 97
  on Mars, 125
Ozone, 99

Pallas (asteroid), 155
Palomar Mountain, 4
Parallax of a star, 198-200
Pare, Ambrose, 162
Parsec, the, 199-200
Peek, Bernard M., 141-142
Pegasus, constellation of, 188
Penumbra of sunspots, 75-76
Perihelion, 106
Period-luminosity relation, 216, 218
Perrotin, 128
Perseids, 187
Perseus, constellation of, 265
Peters, 221
Pettit, Edison, 211
Phobos, 130, 132, 151-152
Photography, of asteroids, 156-157
  astronomy and, 17, 20-24, 80-81, 85-86, 197
  motion-picture, 86-87
Photometers, 195
Piazzi, Giuseppe, 154-155
Plane of the ecliptic, 63
Planets, 16, 18-19
  asteroids and, 160-161
  and Bode's law, 153
  chemical elements of, 108
  and earth, 114-115
  giant, 108-109
  inner, 109-110
  movement of, 109-111, 113
    discovery of, 106

271

Planets, around the sun, 102, 106
 origin of, 190–193
 outer, 110–111, 113–114
 phases of, 113–114
 terrestrial, 31, 108
 velocities of, 102
 (*See also* names of planets, as Mars)
Pluto (planet), 30, 49, 108
 distance from sun, 153
 satellite of, 150–151
 size and mass of, 150
Pointers (stars), 265
Polar caps on Mars, 117–118
Polaris (north star), 265
Pollux (star), 236
Pons, Jean Louis, 176
Porter, Russell W., 56
Poulkovo Observatory, 179–180
Principia, Newton, 107
Prisms, 69–70
Pritchard, the Rev. Charles, 235
Proctor, Richard A., 52, 139, 174
Procyon (star), 202
Proton-proton reaction, 97
Protoplanets, 193

Radio telescopes, 18
Radio waves, 83, 85
 exploration of galaxy and, 252, 254, 257
Radioactivity, 95
Radium, 95
Red giant stars, 203, 214, 220, 231
Red shift, definition of, 257–259
Reflector telescopes, 21–24, 27–28
Refractor telescopes, 21, 27–28
Relativity, theory of, 160, 176
Resisting medium, 177–181
Riccioli, Giovanni Battista, 55
Richey, G. W., 56
Rigel (star), 199, 216
Ring nebula, 17
Rickets, 98–99
Rockets, 56–59
 Russian, 57–58
 velocity of, 58–60
Roemer, Olaus, 145, 147
Rotation, quantity of, 190–191
RR Lyrae stars (*see* Cluster variables)
Russell, H. N., 206

Sagittarius, constellation of, 239–240

Sandage, Allan, 230
Satellites, 108, 149
 artificial, 132
 Galilean, 142
 of Jupiter, 108, 142, 144–145, 147, 157
 of Mars, 130–132, 151
 of Mercury, Venus, and Pluto, 149–152
 of Neptune, 108, 149
 of Saturn, 108
 of Uranus, 149–150
Saturn (planet), 28, 49, 108, 114, 180, 205
 atmosphere of, 148–149
 description of, 147–149
 distance from sun, 153
 gases on, 148–149
 rings of, 147–149, 241
 satellites of, 108
Schiaparelli, Giovanni, 127–128, 185
Schwabe, Heinrich, 15, 78, 141
Scorpio, constellation of, 240, 266
S Doradus (star), 205
Secchi, Father Angelo, 15–17, 201
Shooting stars, 181–182
Sidereal month, 42
Sirius (Dog Star), 195, 199, 202, 216, 222
 brightness of, 221
Sirius B (star), 221–222
 density of, 222–223
Skin cancer, 99
Slipher, V. M., 257–258
Small Magellanic Cloud, 215–216
Solar apex, 210
Solar cycle, 76–77
 eleven-year, discovery of, 78
Solar energy, 66–67
Solar flares, 80–81, 83, 85
Solar granulations, 79–80
Solar prominences, 85–88
Solar radiation (*see* Sunshine)
Solar spectrum, 69–73
Solar system, 187, 190
 asteroids and, 157
 sun and, 65
Space, 261
 exploration of, 251–252, 254, 257
Spectra, 15–16, 69–72
 and Doppler effect, 73–74, 219
 of Sirius B, 223

272

Picture Credits

About the Author

"As early as I can remember," says Dr. Richardson, "I was interested in writing and the stars." So Dr. Richardson became both an astronomer and a writer. After earning his Ph.D. degree in 1931 at the University of California, he joined the staff at Mount Wilson Observatory (later known as The Mount Wilson and Palomar Observatories). Dr. Richardson is now Associate Director of The Griffith Observatory and Planetarium in Los Angeles. He has done a great deal of magazine writing, both fiction and nonfiction, and is the author of *Exploring Mars*, several teen-age books, a college textbook on astronomy, and is co-author of *Sun, Moon, and Stars*.